ATLAS
OF
CONTINENTS

Contents

RAND McNALLY & COMPANY

INTRODUCTION

The *Atlas of Continents* contains thematic maps presenting world patterns and distributions. Together with accompanying graphs, these maps communicate basic information on mineral resources, agricultural products, trade, transportation, and other selected aspects of the natural and cultural geographic environment.

Thematic Maps

A thematic map uses symbols and colors to show certain characteristics of, generally, one class of geographic information. This "theme" of a thematic map is presented upon a background of basic locational information—coastline, country boundaries, major drainage, etc. The map's primary concern is to communicate visually basic impressions of the distribution of the theme.

Real and hypothetical geographical distributions of interest to humans are practically limitless but can be classed into point, line, area, or volume information relative to a specific location or area in the world. To communicate these fundamental classes of information, a thematic map utilizes point, line, and area symbols and colors. The symbols and colors on the maps may show *qualitative* differences (differences in *kind*) of a certain category of information and may also show *quantitative* differences in the information (differences in *amount*).

The statistics communicated by the maps and graphs give an idea of the relative importance of countries in the distributions mapped. The maps are not intended to take the place of statistical reference works. No single year affords a realistic base for production, trade, and certain economic and demographic statistics. Therefore, averages of data for three or four years have been used. Together with the maps, the averages and percentages provide a realistic concept of the importance of specific areas.

Kinds of Maps

The thematic maps in the Atlas of Continents cover a wide range of information. Each depicts the distribution of major natural and human elements that describe the world's fundamental geographic character.

Annual Precipitation
Climate
Demographic
Economic
Education
Energy
Glaciation
Health
Labor Structure
Landforms
Languages
Manufacturing
Minerals
Natural Hazards
Peoples
Physiography
Political
Political Change
Population
Transportation
Types of Farming
Vegetation
Water
Water Resources
Westward Expansion

Because of the range and diversity of topics covered, a variety of symbols and colors was selected to convey specific information. These symbols and colors are defined on each map.

Population in a Different Way

Almost every area of the earth is inhabited by humans, from the Poles to the Equator. It is interesting to note how that population is distributed on the earth, and how the rate of increase in population impacts all humans.

The map shown below, called a cartogram, is a special kind of thematic map. It assigns values to regions based on specific parameters—in this case population and rates of increase—rather than land surface area. In this cartogram, areas assigned are proportional to their countries' populations and tinted according to their rates of increase.

The result is a different way to look at the world. Some nations with relatively small land areas already have vast populations. If current increases continue, these small nations will have a growing impact on the environment.

POPULATION

Note: Size of each country is proportional to population.

Tints indicate rate of natural increase.

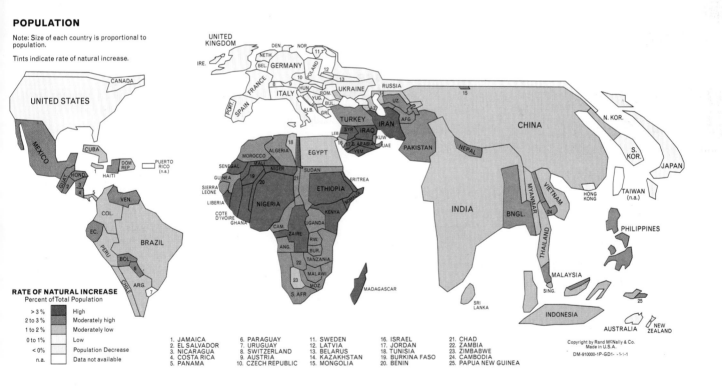

RATE OF NATURAL INCREASE
Percent of Total Population

>3 %	High
2 to 3 %	Moderately high
1 to 2 %	Moderately low
0 to 1%	Low
< 0%	Population Decrease
n.a.	Data not available

1. JAMAICA
2. EL SALVADOR
3. NICARAGUA
4. COSTA RICA
5. PANAMA
6. PARAGUAY
7. URUGUAY
8. SWITZERLAND
9. AUSTRIA
10. CZECH REPUBLIC
11. SWEDEN
12. LATVIA
13. BELARUS
14. KAZAKHSTAN
15. MONGOLIA
16. ISRAEL
17. JORDAN
18. TUNISIA
19. BURKINA FASO
20. BENIN
21. CHAD
22. ZAMBIA
23. ZIMBABWE
24. CAMBODIA
25. PAPUA NEW GUINEA

ENVIRONMENTAL MAPS

The environment maps show the natural environment and how it has been modified by humans. Ten major environments are depicted, and these categories are identified and described in the legend below.

Classification is based upon the appearance and the general activity of an area. In mapping any distribution, however, it is necessary to limit the number of categories. Therefore, some gradations of meaning exist within each category. For example, "Grassland, grazing land" identifies the lush pampas of Argentina and the savannas of Africa as well as the steppes of the Soviet Union. Furthermore, certain enclaves that are not cropland may fall within the boundaries of cropland areas. Tracts such as these are included as part of the dominant environment surrounding them. Finally, boundaries on these maps, as on all maps, are never absolute but mark the center of transitional zones between categories.

The actual shapes of large metropolitan areas are shown. A red dot indicates concentrated urban development where a shape would be indistinguishable at the map scale. Black dots are used to locate places important as locational reference points.

From these maps, comprehensive observations may be made about major world environments. For example, the maps show that the world's urban areas are limited in extent, and relatively small portions of the earth's surface are made up of cropland. Vast areas show the limited influence of humanity upon the environment.

ENVIRONMENTAL MAP LEGEND

URBAN*
Major areas of contiguous residential, commercial and industrial development.

GRASSLAND, GRAZING LAND
Extensive grassland and rangeland with little or no cropland.

TUNDRA
Areas of lichen, shrubs, small trees, and wetland.

CROPLAND
Cultivated land predominates (includes pasture, irrigated land, and land in crop rotation).

OASIS
Important small areas of cultivation within grassland or wasteland.

SHRUB, SPARSE GRASS; WASTELAND
Desert shrub and short grass, growing singly or in patches. Wasteland includes sand, salt flats, etc. (Extensive wastelands shown by pattern.)

CROPLAND AND WOODLAND
Cultivated land interrupted by small wooded areas.

FOREST, WOODLAND
Extensive wooded areas with little or no cropland.

BARREN LAND
Icefields, glaciers, permanent snow, with exposed rock.

CROPLAND AND GRAZING LAND
Cultivated land with grassland and rangeland.

SWAMP, MARSHLAND
Extensive wetland areas (includes mangroves).

*Selected cities as points of reference.

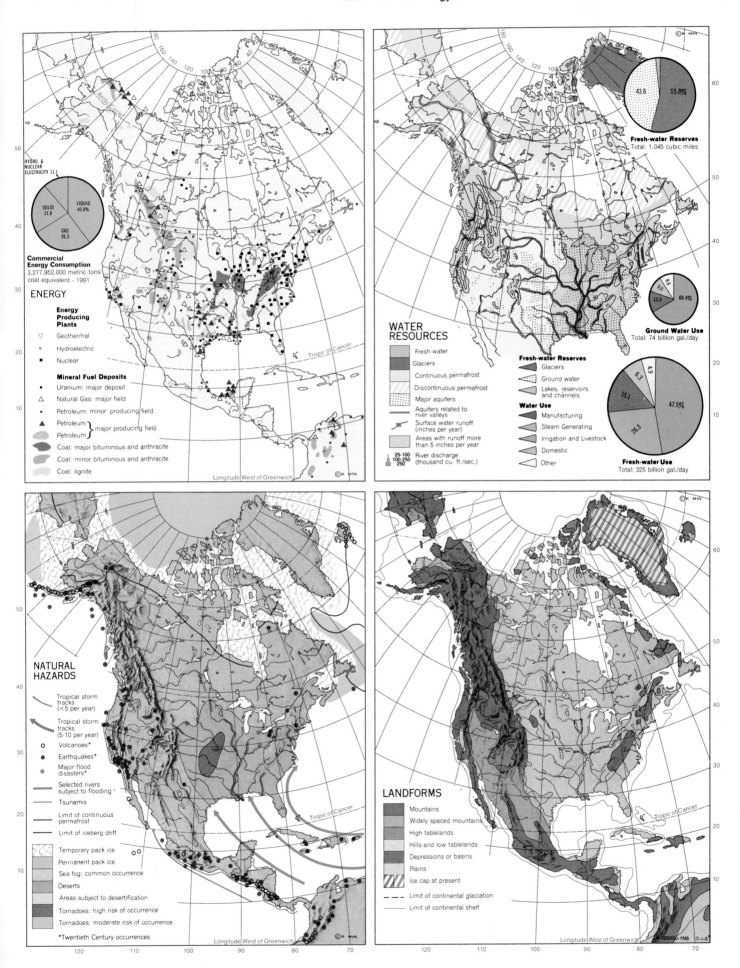

HYDRO. & NUCLEAR ELECTRICITY 11.1

SOLID 21.8
LIQUID 40.8%
GAS 26.3

Commercial Energy Consumption
3,277,952,000 metric tons coal equivalent · 1991

ENERGY

Energy Producing Plants
▽ Geothermal
• Hydroelectric
■ Nuclear

Mineral Fuel Deposits
• Uranium: major deposit
△ Natural Gas: major field
△ Petroleum: minor producing field
▲ Petroleum } major producing field
Petroleum
Coal: major bituminous and anthracite
Coal: minor bituminous and anthracite
Coal: lignite

Longitude West of Greenwich

43.6   55.8%

Fresh-water Reserves
Total: 1,045 cubic miles

8.6
13.9   68.4%

Ground Water Use
Total: 74 billion gal./day

4.9
6.3
15.1   47.5%
26.3

Fresh-water Use
Total: 325 billion gal./day

WATER RESOURCES

Fresh-water
Glaciers
Continuous permafrost
Discontinuous permafrost
Major aquifers
Aquifers related to river valleys
20 — Surface water runoff (inches per year)
Areas with runoff more than 5 inches per year
25-100
100-250
250 River discharge (thousand cu. ft./sec.)

Fresh-water Reserves
▲ Glaciers
▽ Ground water
Lakes, reservoirs and channels
Water Use
Manufacturing
Steam Generating
Irrigation and Livestock
Domestic
Other

NATURAL HAZARDS

Tropical storm tracks (<5 per year)
Tropical storm tracks (5-10 per year)
○ Volcanoes*
● Earthquakes*
● Major flood disasters*
Selected rivers subject to flooding
Tsunamis
Limit of continuous permafrost
Limit of iceberg drift

Temporary pack ice
Permanent pack ice
Sea fog: common occurrence
Deserts
Areas subject to desertification
Tornadoes: high risk of occurrence
Tornadoes: moderate risk of occurrence

*Twentieth Century occurrences

Longitude West of Greenwich

LANDFORMS

Mountains
Widely spaced mountains
High tablelands
Hills and low tablelands
Depressions or basins
Plains
Ice cap at present

– – – Limit of continental glaciation
—— Limit of continental shelf

Longitude West of Greenwich

Tropic of Cancer

120   110   100   90   80   70

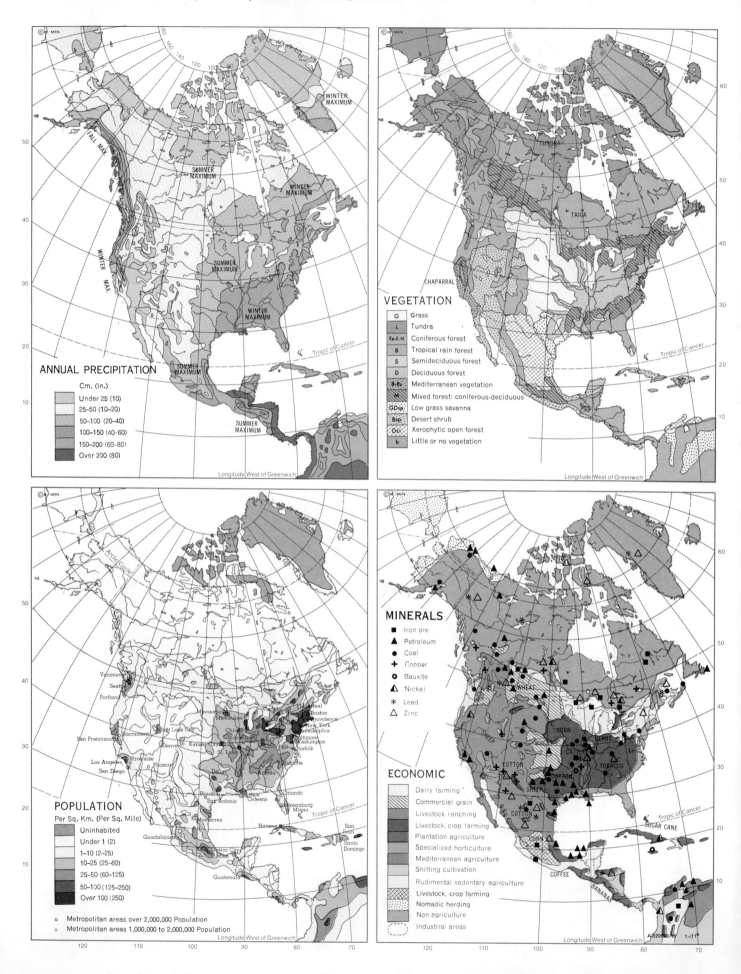

ANNUAL PRECIPITATION

Cm. (In.)

- Under 25 (10)
- 25–50 (10–20)
- 50–100 (20–40)
- 100–150 (40–60)
- 150–200 (60–80)
- Over 200 (80)

VEGETATION

G	Grass
L	Tundra
Ep.E.N	Coniferous forest
B	Tropical rain forest
S	Semideciduous forest
D	Deciduous forest
θ-θs	Mediterranean vegetation
M	Mixed forest: coniferous-deciduous
GDsp	Low grass savanna
Bsp	Desert shrub
Dti	Xerophytic open forest
b	Little or no vegetation

POPULATION

Per Sq. Km. (Per Sq. Mile)

- Uninhabited
- Under 1 (2)
- 1–10 (2–25)
- 10–25 (25–60)
- 25–50 (60–125)
- 50–100 (125–250)
- Over 100 (250)

▫ Metropolitan areas over 2,000,000 Population
○ Metropolitan areas 1,000,000 to 2,000,000 Population

MINERALS

- ■ Iron ore
- ▲ Petroleum
- ● Coal
- ✛ Copper
- ◌ Bauxite
- △ Nickel
- ✳ Lead
- △ Zinc

ECONOMIC

- Dairy farming
- Commercial grain
- Livestock ranching
- Livestock, crop farming
- Plantation agriculture
- Specialized horticulture
- Mediterranean agriculture
- Shifting cultivation
- Rudimental sedentary agriculture
- Livestock, crop farming
- Nomadic herding
- Non agriculture
- Industrial areas

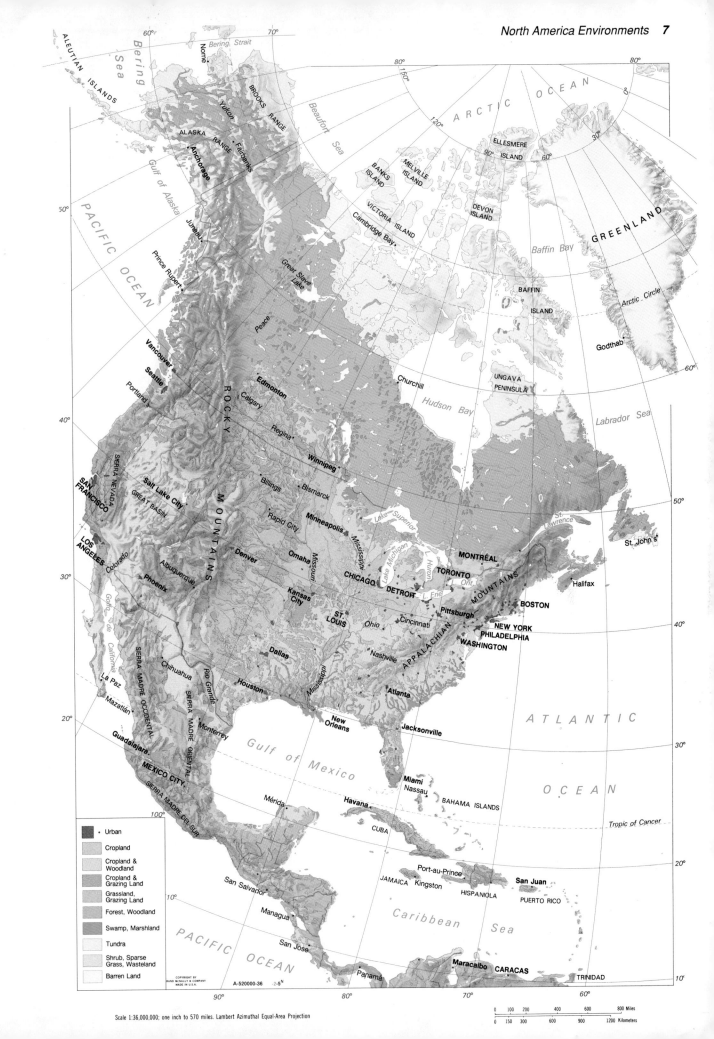

Legend:

- ■ Urban
- Cropland
- Cropland & Woodland
- Cropland & Grazing Land
- Grassland, Grazing Land
- Forest, Woodland
- Swamp, Marshland
- Tundra
- Shrub, Sparse Grass, Wasteland
- Barren Land

COPYRIGHT BY
RAND McNALLY & COMPANY
MADE IN U.S.A.

A-520000-36   -2-5 N

Scale 1:36,000,000; one inch to 570 miles. Lambert Azimuthal Equal-Area Projection

| 0 | 100 | 200 | 400 | 600 | 800 Miles |
| 0 | 150 | 300 | 600 | 900 | 1200 Kilometers |

Labels on map:

ALEUTIAN ISLANDS, Bering Sea, Bering Strait, Nome, Yukon, BROOKS RANGE, Beaufort Sea, ARCTIC OCEAN, ELLESMERE ISLAND, GREENLAND, ALASKA RANGE, Fairbanks, Anchorage, Gulf of Alaska, PACIFIC OCEAN, Juneau, BANKS ISLAND, MELVILLE ISLAND, DEVON ISLAND, Baffin Bay, Prince Rupert, VICTORIA ISLAND, Cambridge Bay, BAFFIN ISLAND, Arctic Circle, Godthab, Great Slave Lake, Vancouver, Seattle, Portland, Peace, ROCKY MOUNTAINS, Edmonton, Calgary, Churchill, Hudson Bay, UNGAVA PENINSULA, Labrador Sea, SAN FRANCISCO, SIERRA NEVADA, Salt Lake City, GREAT BASIN, Regina, Winnipeg, St. Lawrence, St. John's, LOS ANGELES, Colorado, Denver, Billings, Bismarck, Minneapolis, Lake Superior, Rapid City, Omaha, Missouri, Mississippi, Lake Michigan, Huron, MONTRÉAL, Ont., TORONTO, Halifax, Phoenix, Albuquerque, Kansas City, CHICAGO, DETROIT, L. Erie, APPALACHIAN MOUNTAINS, BOSTON, Pittsburgh, NEW YORK, PHILADELPHIA, ST. LOUIS, Ohio, Cincinnati, WASHINGTON, Chihuahua, Rio Grande, Dallas, Nashville, SIERRA MADRE OCCIDENTAL, La Paz, Golfo de California, Mazatlán, Monterrey, SIERRA MADRE ORIENTAL, Houston, Mississippi, Atlanta, New Orleans, Jacksonville, Guadalajara, MEXICO CITY, SIERRA MADRE DEL SUR, Gulf of Mexico, Miami, Nassau, BAHAMA ISLANDS, ATLANTIC OCEAN, Tropic of Cancer, Mérida, Havana, CUBA, San Salvador, Managua, San Jose, Panamá, PACIFIC OCEAN, Port-au-Prince, JAMAICA, Kingston, HISPANIOLA, San Juan, PUERTO RICO, Caribbean Sea, Maracaibo, CARACAS, TRINIDAD

8

PACIFIC OCEAN

PACIFIC OCEAN

Vancouver

Seattle

Spokane

Portland

Columbia

CASCADE RANGE

Medford

Boise

SIERRA NEVADA

Reno

SAN FRANCISCO

GREAT BASIN

Great Salt Lake

Salt Lake City

Fresno

Las Vegas

LOS ANGELES

San Diego

Colorado

Phoenix

Hermosillo

Gulf of California

SIERRA MADRE OCCIDENTAL

Chihuahua

Torreón

ROCKY MOUNTAINS

Calgary

Regina

Billings

Rapid City

Casper

Denver

Albuquerque

Amarillo

El Paso

Odessa

Rio Grande

SIERRA MADRE ORIENTAL

Monterrey

Bismarck

Lake Winnipeg

Wir

Omal

Wichita

Oklahoma City

Red

San Antonio

Rio Grande

Missouri

D

50°

45°

40°

35°

30°

25°

125°

120°

115°

130°

125°

120°

115°

110°

105°

100°

A-520500-36 -1-1-3ᴺ
COPYRIGHT BY
RAND MCNALLY & COMPANY
MADE IN U.S.A.

Scale 1:12,000,000; one inch to 190 miles.
Albers Conical Equal Area Projection

0	50 100	200 300 400 Miles
0	75 150	300 450 600 Kilometers

Legend:
- Urban
- Cropland
- Cropland & Woodland
- Cropland & Grazing Land
- Grassland, Grazing Land
- Forest, Woodland
- Swamp, Marshland
- Shrub, Sparse Grass, Wasteland
- Barren Land

10

PHYSIOGRAPHIC DIVISIONS

1 Pacific Mountain System
2 Intermontane Plateaus
3 Rocky Mountain System
4 Interior Plains
5 Ozark-Ouachita Highlands
6 Gulf-Atlantic Plain
7 Appalachian Highlands
8 Laurentian Upland (Canadian Shield)
9 Hudson Bay Lowland

Scale 1: 12 000 000; One inch to 190 miles.   POLYCONIC PROJECTION

PHYSIOGRAPHY
BY
ERWIN RAISZ

LITHOLOGY AND STRUCTURE

Unconsolidated deposits: alluvium, sands, playa deposits, etc.

Essentially horizontal sedimentary rocks; many partially unconsolidated.

Slightly to moderately tilted, older sedimentary rocks.

Steeply folded or faulted, sedimentary rocks

Volcanics; largely lava flows.

Metamorphic and intrusive igneous rocks; structure complex.

Limits of continental glaciation.

LANDFORMS

PLATEAUS

HILLS

MOUNTAINS

MESAS

CUESTAS

FOLDED MOUNTAINS

BASIN RANGES

VOLCANO AND LAVA

SAND

SINKS

MORAINES

DRUMLINS

A-520500-762 -3 - 352
Copyright by Rand McNally & Co.
Made in U.S.A.

itude West of Greenwich

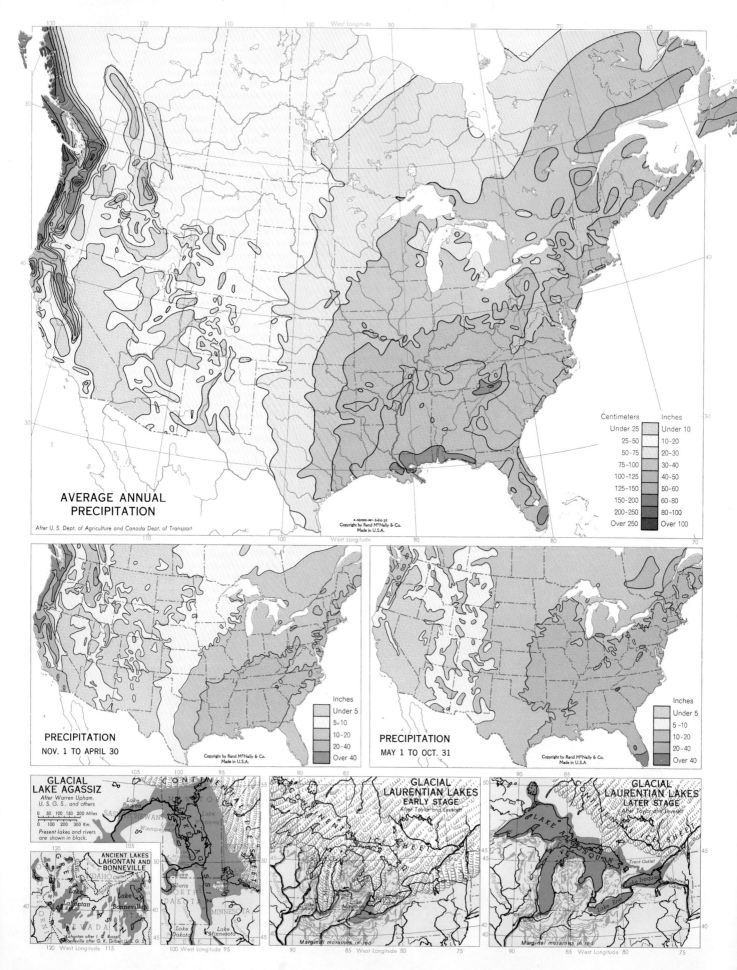

AVERAGE ANNUAL PRECIPITATION

After U. S. Dept. of Agriculture and Canada Dept. of Transport

Copyright by Rand McNally & Co.
Made in U.S.A.

Centimeters	Inches
Under 25	Under 10
25-50	10-20
50-75	20-30
75-100	30-40
100-125	40-50
125-150	50-60
150-200	60-80
200-250	80-100
Over 250	Over 100

PRECIPITATION
NOV. 1 TO APRIL 30

Copyright by Rand McNally & Co.
Made in U.S.A.

Inches
Under 5
5-10
10-20
20-40
Over 40

PRECIPITATION
MAY 1 TO OCT. 31

Copyright by Rand McNally & Co.
Made in U.S.A.

Inches
Under 5
5-10
10-20
20-40
Over 40

GLACIAL LAKE AGASSIZ
After Warren Upham, U. S. G. S. and others

0 50 100 150 200 Miles
0 100 200 300 Km.

Present lakes and rivers are shown in black.

ANCIENT LAKES LAHONTAN AND BONNEVILLE
Lahontan after I. C. Russell
Bonneville after G. K. Gilbert, U.S.G.S.

GLACIAL LAURENTIAN LAKES
EARLY STAGE
After Taylor and Leverett

Marginal moraines in red

GLACIAL LAURENTIAN LAKES
LATER STAGE
After Taylor and Leverett

Marginal moraines in red

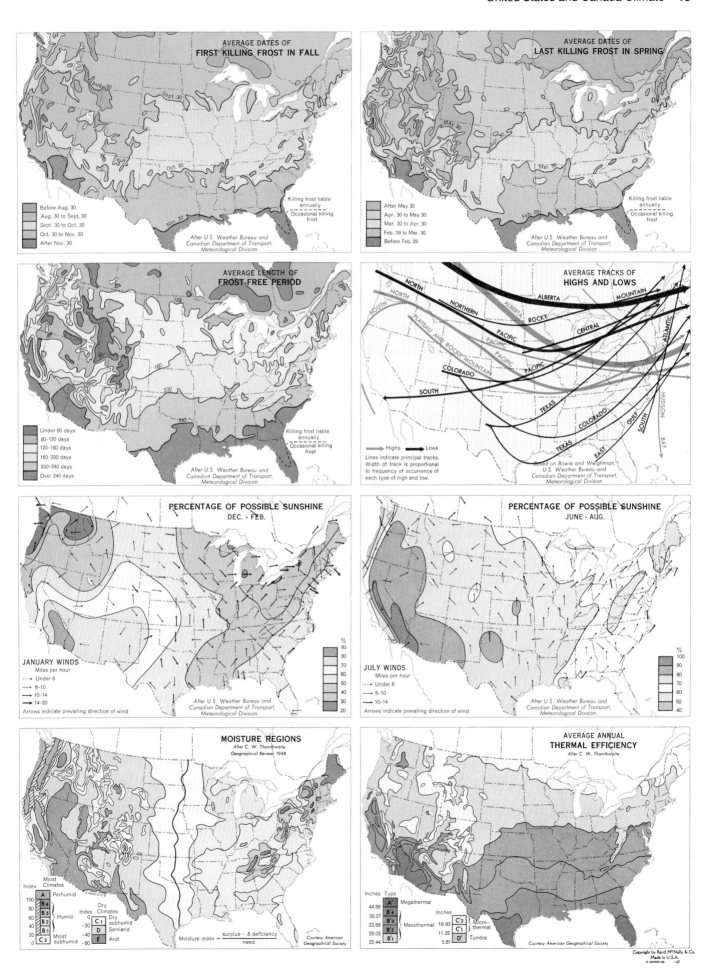

AVERAGE DATES OF
FIRST KILLING FROST IN FALL

Before Aug. 30
Aug. 30 to Sept. 30
Sept. 30 to Oct. 30
Oct. 30 to Nov. 30
After Nov. 30

Killing frost liable
annually
Occasional killing
frost

After U.S. Weather Bureau and
Canadian Department of Transport,
Meteorological Division

AVERAGE DATES OF
LAST KILLING FROST IN SPRING

After May 30
Apr. 30 to May 30
Mar. 30 to Apr. 30
Feb. 28 to Mar. 30
Before Feb. 28

Killing frost liable
annually
Occasional killing
frost

After U.S. Weather Bureau and
Canadian Department of Transport,
Meteorological Division

AVERAGE LENGTH OF
FROST-FREE PERIOD

Under 80 days
80–120 days
120–160 days
160–200 days
200–240 days
Over 240 days

Killing frost liable
annually
Occasional killing
frost

After U.S. Weather Bureau and
Canadian Department of Transport,
Meteorological Division

AVERAGE TRACKS OF
HIGHS AND LOWS

Highs   Lows

Lines indicate principal tracks.
Width of track is proportional
to frequency of occurrence of
each type of high and low.

Based on Bowie and Weightman,
U.S. Weather Bureau and
Canadian Department of Transport,
Meteorological Division

PERCENTAGE OF POSSIBLE SUNSHINE
DEC. – FEB.

JANUARY WINDS
Miles per hour
- - - Under 6
6–10
10–14
14–20
Arrows indicate prevailing direction of wind

%
90
80
70
60
50
40
30
20

PERCENTAGE OF POSSIBLE SUNSHINE
JUNE – AUG.

JULY WINDS
Miles per hour
- - - Under 6
6–10
10–14
Arrows indicate prevailing direction of wind

%
100
90
80
70
60
50
40

After U.S. Weather Bureau and
Canadian Department of Transport,
Meteorological Division

MOISTURE REGIONS
After C. W. Thornthwaite
Geographical Review, 1948

Index   Moist
Climates
100 A   Perhumid
80   B4
60   B3   Humid
40   B2
20   B1
0   C2   Moist
          subhumid

Index   Dry
Climates
0   C1   Dry
          subhumid
-20 D   Semiarid
-40 E   Arid
-60

Moisture index = $\dfrac{\text{surplus} - .6 \text{ deficiency}}{\text{need}}$

Courtesy American
Geographical Society

AVERAGE ANNUAL
THERMAL EFFICIENCY
After C. W. Thornthwaite

Inches Type
44.88   A'   Megathermal
39.27   B'4
33.66   B'3   Mesothermal
28.05   B'2
22.44   B'1

Inches
16.83   C'2   Micro-
11.22   C'1   thermal
5.61   D'   Tundra

Courtesy American Geographical Society

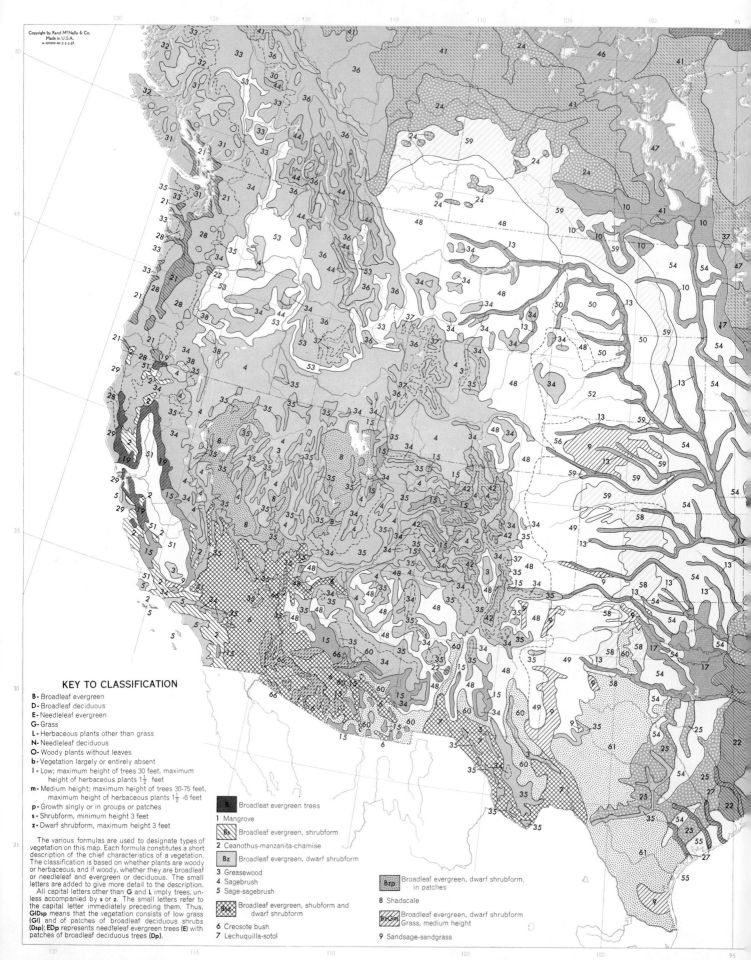

Copyright by Rand McNally & Co.
Made in U.S.A.
A-520500-94-2-2-2-37

KEY TO CLASSIFICATION

B- Broadleaf evergreen
D- Broadleaf deciduous
E- Needleleaf evergreen
G- Grass
L- Herbaceous plants other than grass
N- Needleleaf deciduous
O- Woody plants without leaves
b- Vegetation largely or entirely absent
l- Low; maximum height of trees 30 feet, maximum
    height of herbaceous plants 1½ feet
m- Medium height; maximum height of trees 30-75 feet,
    maximum height of herbaceous plants 1½ -6 feet
p- Growth singly or in groups or patches
s- Shrubform, minimum height 3 feet
z- Dwarf shrubform, maximum height 3 feet

The various formulas are used to designate types of
vegetation on this map. Each formula constitutes a short
description of the chief characteristics of a vegetation.
The classification is based on whether plants are woody
or herbaceous, and if woody, whether they are broadleaf
or needleleaf and evergreen or deciduous. The small
letters are added to give more detail to the description.
    All capital letters other than **G** and **L** imply trees, un-
less accompanied by **s** or **z**. The small letters refer to
the capital letter immediately preceding them. Thus,
GlDsp means that the vegetation consists of low grass
(**Gl**) and of patches of broadleaf deciduous shrubs
(**Dsp**); **EDp** represents needleleaf evergreen trees (**E**) with
patches of broadleaf deciduous trees (**Dp**).

B Broadleaf evergreen trees
1 Mangrove
Bs Broadleaf evergreen, shrubform
2 Ceanothus-manzanita-chamise
Bz Broadleaf evergreen, dwarf shrubform
3 Greasewood
4 Sagebrush
5 Sage-sagebrush
Bsz Broadleaf evergreen, shubform and
      dwarf shrubform
6 Creosote bush
7 Lechuquilla-sotol

8 Shadscale

Bzp Broadleaf evergreen, dwarf shrubform,
      in patches

BzGm Broadleaf evergreen, dwarf shrubform
       Grass, medium height
9 Sandsage-sandgrass

Scale 1:14 000 000;   One inch to 220

0 25 50 U.S.A 100   200   300   400   500 Miles

0 50 100   200   400   600   800 Kilometers

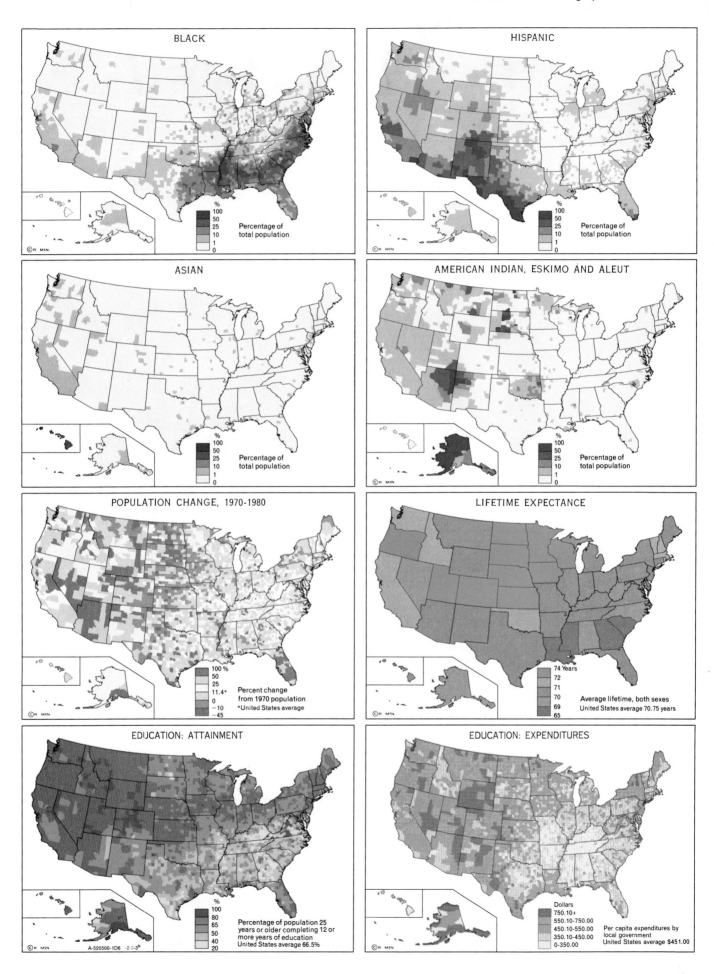

BLACK

%
100
50
25
10
1
0
Percentage of
total population

HISPANIC

%
100
50
25
10
1
0
Percentage of
total population

ASIAN

%
100
50
25
10
1
0
Percentage of
total population

AMERICAN INDIAN, ESKIMO AND ALEUT

%
100
50
25
10
1
0
Percentage of
total population

POPULATION CHANGE, 1970-1980

100 %
50
25
11.4*
0
-10
-45
Percent change
from 1970 population
*United States average

LIFETIME EXPECTANCE

74 Years
72
71
70
69
65
Average lifetime, both sexes
United States average 70.75 years

EDUCATION: ATTAINMENT

%
100
80
65
50
40
20
Percentage of population 25
years or older completing 12 or
more years of education
United States average 66.5%

A-520500-1D6 -2-2-3ᴺ

EDUCATION: EXPENDITURES

Dollars
750.10+
550.10-750.00
450.10-550.00
350.10-450.00
0-350.00
Per capita expenditures by
local government
United States average $451.00

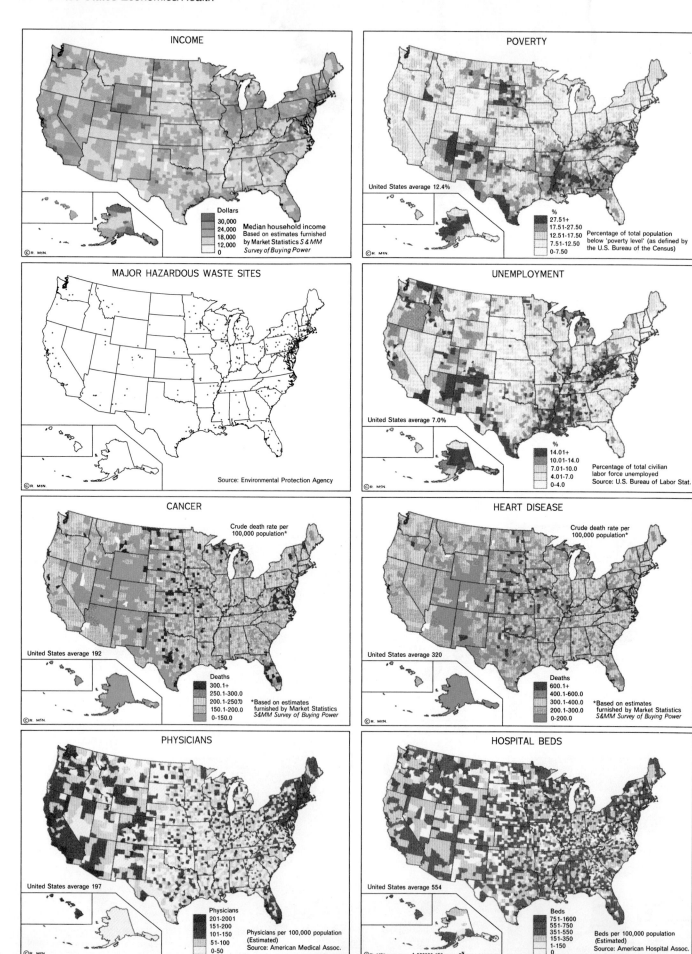

INCOME

Dollars
30,000
24,000
18,000
12,000
0
Median household income
Based on estimates furnished
by Market Statistics S & MM
Survey of Buying Power

POVERTY

United States average 12.4%

%
27.51+
17.51-27.50
12.51-17.50
7.51-12.50
0-7.50
Percentage of total population
below 'poverty level' (as defined by
the U.S. Bureau of the Census)

MAJOR HAZARDOUS WASTE SITES

Source: Environmental Protection Agency

UNEMPLOYMENT

United States average 7.0%

%
14.01+
10.01-14.0
7.01-10.0
4.01-7.0
0-4.0
Percentage of total civilian
labor force unemployed
Source: U.S. Bureau of Labor Stat.

CANCER

Crude death rate per
100,000 population*

United States average 192

Deaths
300.1+
250.1-300.0
200.1-250.0
150.1-200.0
0-150.0
*Based on estimates
furnished by Market Statistics
S&MM Survey of Buying Power

HEART DISEASE

Crude death rate per
100,000 population*

United States average 320

Deaths
600.1+
400.1-600.0
300.1-400.0
200.1-300.0
0-200.0
*Based on estimates
furnished by Market Statistics
S&MM Survey of Buying Power

PHYSICIANS

United States average 197

Physicians
201-2001
151-200
101-150
51-100
0-50
Physicians per 100,000 population
(Estimated)
Source: American Medical Assoc.

HOSPITAL BEDS

United States average 554

Beds
751-1600
551-750
351-550
151-350
1-150
0
Beds per 100,000 population
(Estimated)
Source: American Hospital Assoc.

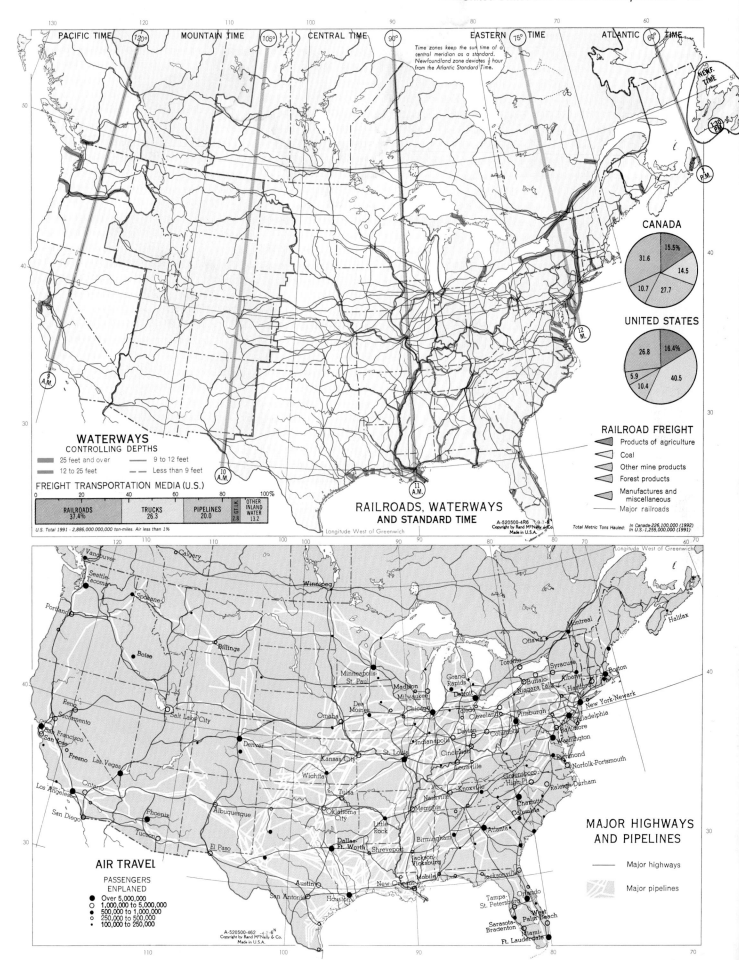

PACIFIC TIME   MOUNTAIN TIME   CENTRAL TIME   EASTERN TIME   ATLANTIC TIME

Time zones keep the sun time of a central meridian as a standard. Newfoundland zone deviates $\frac{1}{2}$ hour from the Atlantic Standard Time.

CANADA

UNITED STATES

WATERWAYS
CONTROLLING DEPTHS

25 feet and over   9 to 12 feet
12 to 25 feet   Less than 9 feet

FREIGHT TRANSPORTATION MEDIA (U.S.)

| RAILROADS 37.4% | TRUCKS 26.3 | PIPELINES 20.0 | GT.LK. 2.8 | OTHER INLAND WATER 13.2 |

U.S. Total 1991 - 2,886,000,000,000 ton-miles. Air less than 1%

RAILROAD FREIGHT

Products of agriculture
Coal
Other mine products
Forest products
Manufactures and miscellaneous
Major railroads

RAILROADS, WATERWAYS AND STANDARD TIME

A-520500-4R6
Copyright by Rand McNally & Co.
Made in U.S.A.

Total Metric Tons Hauled: In Canada-226,100,000 (1992)
In U.S.-1,255,000,000 (1991)

Longitude West of Greenwich

Longitude West of Greenwich

MAJOR HIGHWAYS AND PIPELINES

Major highways

Major pipelines

AIR TRAVEL

PASSENGERS ENPLANED

Over 5,000,000
1,000,000 to 5,000,000
500,000 to 1,000,000
250,000 to 500,000
100,000 to 250,000

A-520500-462
Copyright by Rand McNally & Co.
Made in U.S.A.

Scale 1: 28 000 000; One inch to 440 miles.   LAMBERT CONFORMAL CONIC PROJECTION

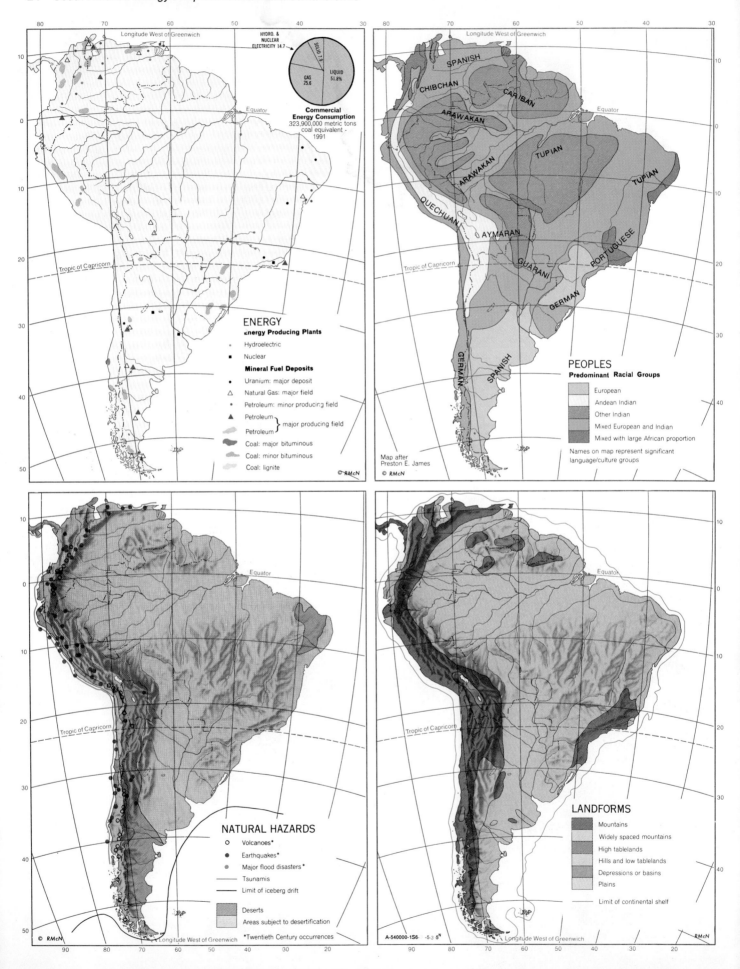

ENERGY

Energy Producing Plants

- ▪ Hydroelectric
- ■ Nuclear

Mineral Fuel Deposits

- • Uranium: major deposit
- △ Natural Gas: major field
- • Petroleum: minor producing field
- ▲ Petroleum
- Petroleum } major producing field
- Coal: major bituminous
- Coal: minor bituminous
- Coal: lignite

© RMcN

HYDRO. & NUCLEAR ELECTRICITY 14.7

SOLID 7.9

GAS 25.6

LIQUID 51.8%

Commercial Energy Consumption
323,900,000 metric tons coal equivalent - 1991

PEOPLES

Predominant Racial Groups

- European
- Andean Indian
- Other Indian
- Mixed European and Indian
- Mixed with large African proportion

Names on map represent significant language/culture groups

Map after Preston E. James

© RMcN

NATURAL HAZARDS

- ○ Volcanoes*
- ● Earthquakes*
- ● Major flood disasters *
- —— Tsunamis
- —— Limit of iceberg drift
- Deserts
- Areas subject to desertification

*Twentieth Century occurrences

© RMcN

LANDFORMS

- Mountains
- Widely spaced mountains
- High tablelands
- Hills and low tablelands
- Depressions or basins
- Plains
- —— Limit of continental shelf

A-540000-1S6- -5-3 5ᴺ

RMcN

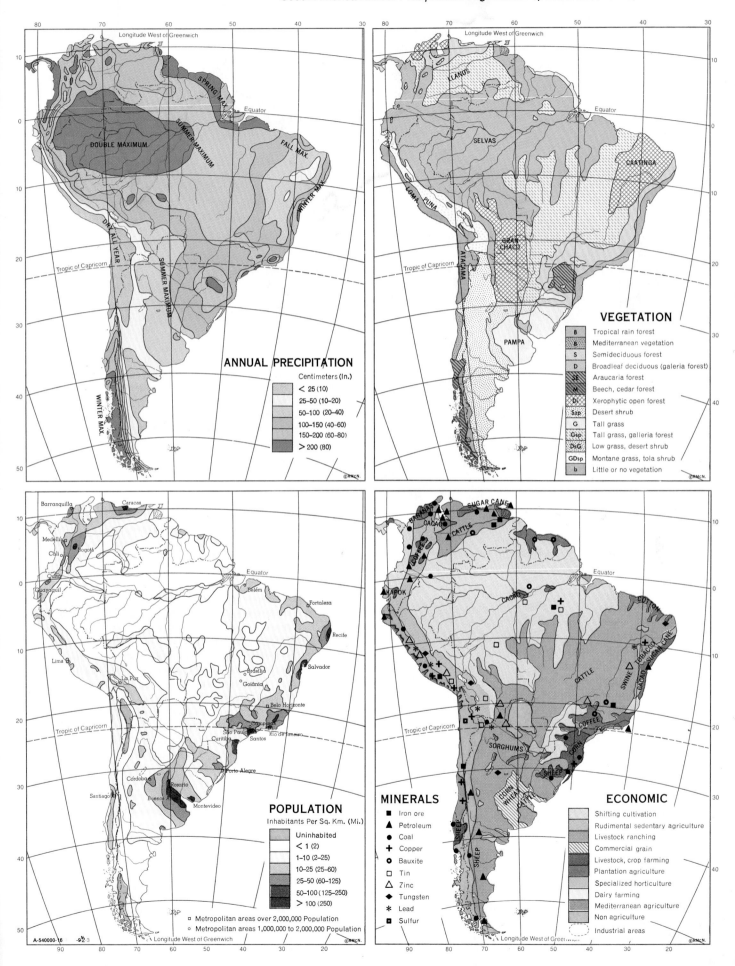

ANNUAL PRECIPITATION

Centimeters (In.)

- < 25 (10)
- 25–50 (10–20)
- 50–100 (20–40)
- 100–150 (40–60)
- 150–200 (60–80)
- > 200 (80)

VEGETATION

B	Tropical rain forest
B	Mediterranean vegetation
S	Semideciduous forest
D	Broadleaf deciduous (galeria forest)
SE	Araucaria forest
M	Beech, cedar forest
D	Xerophytic open forest
Szp	Desert shrub
G	Tall grass
Gsp	Tall grass, galleria forest
DsG	Low grass, desert shrub
GDsp	Montane grass, tola shrub
b	Little or no vegetation

POPULATION

Inhabitants Per Sq. Km. (Mi.)

- Uninhabited
- < 1 (2)
- 1–10 (2–25)
- 10–25 (25–60)
- 25–50 (60–125)
- 50–100 (125–250)
- > 100 (250)

□ Metropolitan areas over 2,000,000 Population
○ Metropolitan areas 1,000,000 to 2,000,000 Population

MINERALS

- ■ Iron ore
- ▲ Petroleum
- ● Coal
- + Copper
- ◎ Bauxite
- □ Tin
- △ Zinc
- ◆ Tungsten
- ✳ Lead
- ▪ Sulfur

ECONOMIC

- Shifting cultivation
- Rudimental sedentary agriculture
- Livestock ranching
- Commercial grain
- Livestock, crop farming
- Plantation agriculture
- Specialized horticulture
- Dairy farming
- Mediterranean agriculture
- Non agriculture
- Industrial areas

A-540000-16   -9 2 3

CUBA
JAMAICA
Kingston
HISPANIOLA
San Juan
PUERTO RICO
Caribbean Sea
Barranquilla
Maracaibo
CARACAS
Port of Spain
TRINIDAD
Panamá
LLANOS
Orinoco
Georgetown
SANTA FE DE BOGOTÁ
Quito
Negro
Equator
Iquitos
Amazon
Manaus
Belém
Fortaleza
S E L V A S
A N D E S
Rio Branco
São Francisco
Recife
LIMA
La Paz
Cuiabá
M A T O G R O S S O
Brasília
Salvador
Iquique
G R A N C H A C O
Paraná
Belo Horizonte
Tropic of Capricorn
Asunción
SÃO PAULO
RIO DE JANEIRO
San Miguel de Tucumán
Córdoba
Pórto Alegre
SANTIAGO
BUENOS AIRES
Montevideo
PAMPA
Bahía Blanca
P A T A G O N I A
Puerto Montt
P A C I F I C O C E A N
FALKLAND ISLANDS
Punta Arenas
TIERRA DEL FUEGO
Drake Passage
SOUTH GEORGIA
A T L A N T I C O C E A N
A T L A N T I C O C E A N

Legend:
- Urban
- Cropland
- Cropland & Woodland
- Cropland & Grazing Land
- Grassland, Grazing Land
- Forest, Woodland
- Swamp, Marshland
- Shrub, Sparse Grass, Wasteland
- Barren Land

A-540000-36   -2-6
COPYRIGHT BY
RAND McNALLY & COMPANY
MADE IN U.S.A.

Scale 1:36,000,000; one inch to 570 miles Lambert Azimuthal Equal-Area Projection

0   100   200   400   600   800 Miles
0   150   300   600   900   1200 Kilometers

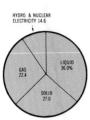

HYDRO. & NUCLEAR
ELECTRICITY 14.6

GAS
22.4

LIQUID
36.0%

SOLID
27.0

**Commercial
Energy Consumption**
2,768,953,000 metric tons
coal equivalent - 1991

ENERGY

Energy Producing Plants

▽ Geothermal

· Hydroelectric

■ Nuclear

Mineral Fuel Deposits

· Uranium: major deposit

△ Natural Gas: major field

· Petroleum: minor producing field

▲ Petroleum ⎫
            ⎬ major producing field
   Petroleum ⎭

   Coal: major bituminous and anthracite

   Coal: minor bituminous and anthracite

   Coal: lignite

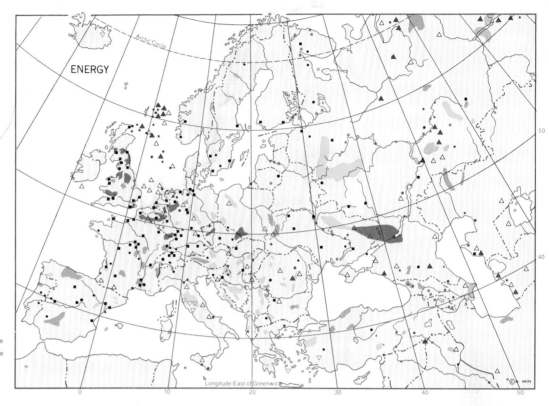

ENERGY

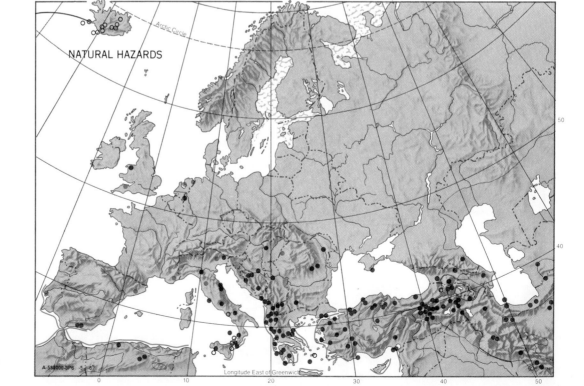

NATURAL HAZARDS

NATURAL HAZARDS

○ Volcanoes*

● Earthquakes*

● Major flood disasters*

— Tsunamis

— Limit of iceberg drift

   Temporary pack ice

   Areas subject to desertification

   *Twentieth Century occurrences

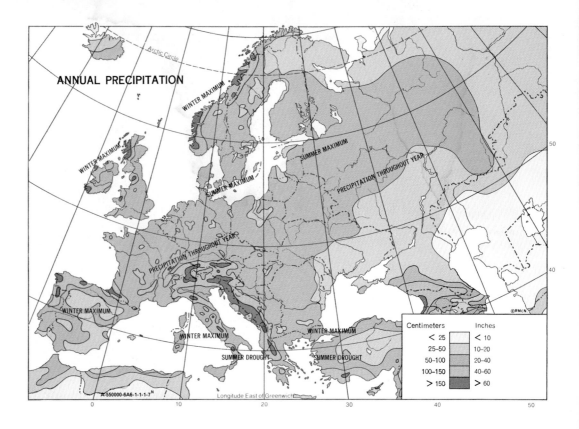

ANNUAL PRECIPITATION

WINTER MAXIMUM

WINTER MAXIMUM

SUMMER MAXIMUM

SUMMER MAXIMUM

PRECIPITATION THROUGHOUT YEAR

PRECIPITATION THROUGHOUT YEAR

WINTER MAXIMUM

WINTER MAXIMUM

WINTER MAXIMUM

SUMMER DROUGHT

SUMMER DROUGHT

Centimeters	Inches
< 25	< 10
25–50	10–20
50–100	20–40
100–150	40–60
> 150	> 60

A-550000-6A6-1-1-1-7

Longitude East of Greenwich

VEGETATION

TAIGA

STEPPE

VEGETATION

E	Coniferous forest
B,Bs	Mediterranean vegetation
M	Mixed forest: coniferous-deciduous
S	Semi-deciduous forest
D	Deciduous forest
DG	Wooded steppe
G	Grass (steppe)
Gp	Short grass
Dsp	Desert shrub
L	Heath and moor
L	Alpine vegetation, tundra
b	Little or no vegetation

A-550000-86-1-1-1-6

Longitude East of Greenwich

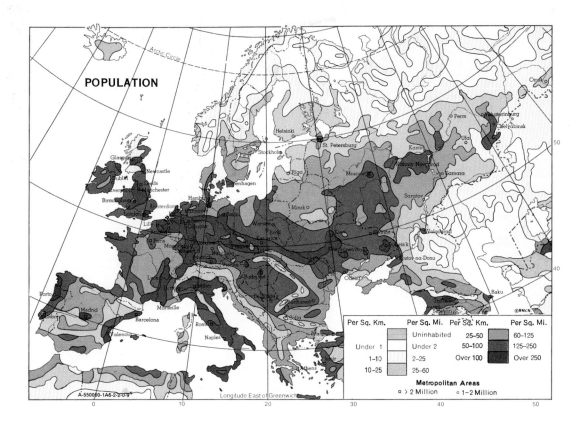

POPULATION

Per Sq. Km.	Per Sq. Mi.	Per Sq. Km.	Per Sq. Mi.
	Uninhabited	25–50	60–125
Under 1	Under 2	50–100	125–250
1–10	2–25	Over 100	Over 250
10–25	25–60		

Metropolitan Areas
□ > 2 Million   ○ 1–2 Million

A-550000-1A6-2-2-0-8   Longitude East of Greenwich

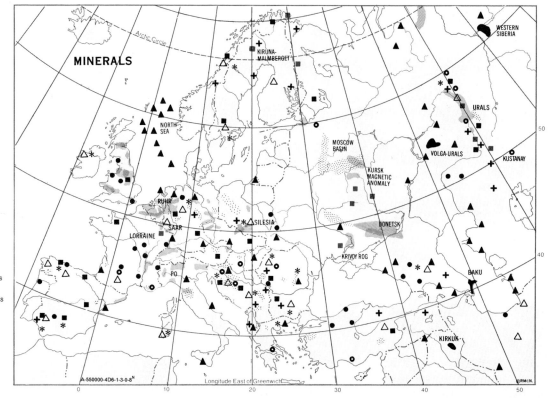

MINERALS

Industrial areas
Major coal deposits
● Major petroleum deposits
Lignite deposits
▲ Minor petroleum deposits
● Minor coal deposits
■ Major iron ore
■ Minor iron ore
✳ Lead
◉ Bauxite
△ Zinc
+ Copper

A-550000-4D6-1-3-0-8   Longitude East of Greenwich

Urban

Cropland

Cropland & Woodland

Cropland & Grazing Land

Grassland, Grazing Land

Forest, Woodland

Swamp, Marshland

Tundra

Shrub, Sparse Grass,
Wasteland (pattern)

Barren Land

Oasis

ATLANTIC OCEAN

Reykjavik

Narvik

Trondheim

Bergen

Oslo

Göteborg

Helsinki

ST. PETERSBURG

Tallinn

Stockholm

Riga

North Sea

Gulf of Bothnia

Glasgow

Belfast

MANCHESTER

Dublin

Copenhagen

Baltic Sea

Kaliningrad

Vilnius

Minsk

Amsterdam

Hamburg

Elbe

BERLIN

Warsaw

LONDON

Antwerp

Essen

Leipzig

Oder

Brest

Frankfurt

Prague

Kraków

L'viv

PARIS

Seine

Strasbourg

Rhine

Danube

VIENNA

CARPATHIANS

Loire

Bay of Biscay

Munich

Zürich

Lyon

A L P S

MILAN

BUDAPEST

Tisza

La Coruña

Bordeaux

Garonne

Bilbao

Rhône

Venice

Zagreb

Sava

Belgrade

Bucharest

Douro

PYRENEES

Ebro

Marseille

Genoa

Adriatic Sea

Danube

Lisbon

MADRID

BARCELONA

CORSICA

ROME

Sofia

Sevilla

SARDINIA

ISLAS BALEARES

Tyrrhenian Sea

Naples

Tirane

Aegean Sea

Tanger

M e d i t e r r a n e a n

Palermo

Athens

Casablanca

Oran

Algiers

ATLAS MOUNTAINS

Tunis

SICILY

S e a

MALTA

CRETE

Longitude West of Greenwich   0°   Longitude East of Greenwich

Scale 1: 16,000,000; one inch to 250 miles. Conic Projection

0 50 100   200   300   400   500 Miles

0   100   200   400   600   800 Kilometers

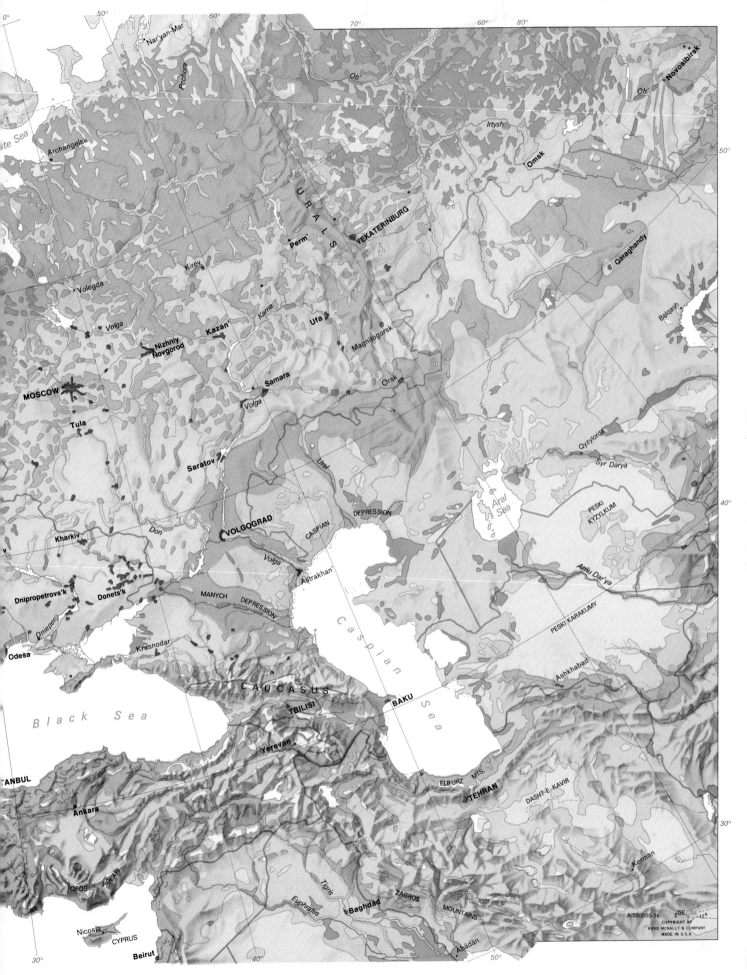

Nar'yan-Mar

Pechora

te Sea

Archangelsk

Ob'

Irtysh

Omsk

Novosibirsk

Ob'

U R A L S

YEKATERINBURG

Perm

Vologda

Kirov

Kama

Ufa

Volga

Kazan'

Nizhniy Novgorod

Magnitogorsk

Qaraghandy

Balqash

MOSCOW

Samara

Orsk

Volga

Tula

Saratov

Ural

Qyzylorda

Syr Darya

Aral Sea

PESKI KYZYLKUM

DEPRESSION

Kharkiv

Don

VOLGOGRAD

CASPIAN

Amu Dar'ya

Dnipropetrovs'k

Donets'k

MANYCH

DEPRESSION

Volga

Astrakhan'

PESKI KARAKUMY

Dnieper

Krasnodar

Caspian

Ashkhabad

Odesa

C A U C A S U S

Sea

BAKU

Black   Sea

TBILISI

Yerevan

ELBURZ   MTS.

DASHT-E KAVIR

ANBUL

Ankara

TEHRAN

Kerman

TOROS

AGRI

Tigris

ZAGROS

Nicosia

CYPRUS

Euphrates

Baghdad

MOUNTAINS

Beirut

Abādān

Scale 1:16 000 000; one inch to 250 miles. Conic Projection
Elevations and depressions are given in feet.

PHYSIOGRAPHIC PROVINCES

0 ___ 400
Miles

Western Uplands (Mostly old rocks) | Great European Plain | Central Uplands | Alpine System

EUROPE DURING THE ICE AGE

Tundra | Forest | Steppe

PHYSIOGRAPHY
BY
ERWIN RAISZ

LITHOLOGY AND STRUCTURE

Unconsolidated deposits: alluvium, sands, bottom lands.

Strongly folded and faulted rocks. The "Younger Series" in Norway.

Essentially horizontal sediments, also uplands and terraces in the plains.

Metamorphic and intrusive igneous rocks.

Moderately folded sedimentary rocks.

volcanics, lava flows, basalts, etc.

LANDFORMS

PLATEAUS | CUESTAS | SAND

HILLS | FOLDED MOUNTAINS | SINKS

MOUNTAINS | BASIN RANGES | MORAINES

MESAS | VOLCANO AND LAVA | DRUMLINS

0 50 100 200 300 400 500 Miles

0 200 400 600 800 Kilometers

EUROPE LANGUAGES
BY
BOGDAN ZABORSKI

Scale 1:16,500,000; one inch to 260 miles Conic Projection

0   100   200   300   400   500   600   Miles
0   200   400   600   800   1000 Kilometers

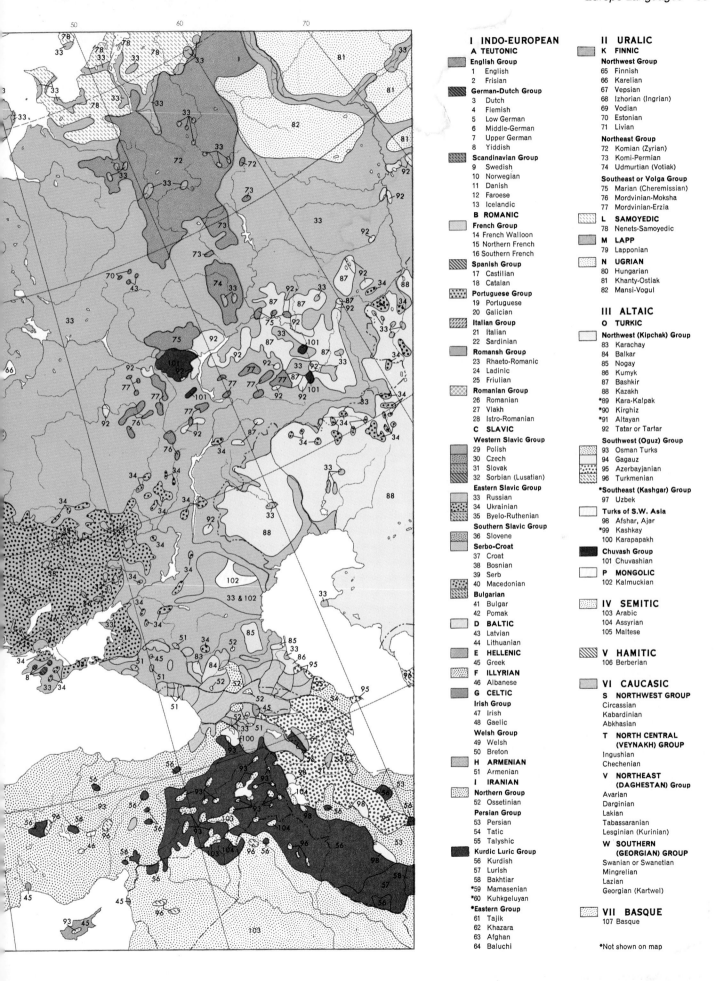

I INDO-EUROPEAN

A TEUTONIC

English Group
1 English
2 Frisian

German-Dutch Group
3 Dutch
4 Flemish
5 Low German
6 Middle-German
7 Upper German
8 Yiddish

Scandinavian Group
9 Swedish
10 Norwegian
11 Danish
12 Faroese
13 Icelandic

B ROMANIC

French Group
14 French Walloon
15 Northern French
16 Southern French

Spanish Group
17 Castilian
18 Catalan

Portuguese Group
19 Portuguese
20 Galician

Italian Group
21 Italian
22 Sardinian

Romansh Group
23 Rhaeto-Romanic
24 Ladinic
25 Friulian

Romanian Group
26 Romanian
27 Vlakh
28 Istro-Romanian

C SLAVIC

Western Slavic Group
29 Polish
30 Czech
31 Slovak
32 Sorbian (Lusatian)

Eastern Slavic Group
33 Russian
34 Ukrainian
35 Byelo-Ruthenian

Southern Slavic Group
36 Slovene

Serbo-Croat
37 Croat
38 Bosnian
39 Serb
40 Macedonian

Bulgarian
41 Bulgar
42 Pomak

D BALTIC
43 Latvian
44 Lithuanian

E HELLENIC
45 Greek

F ILLYRIAN
46 Albanese

G CELTIC

Irish Group
47 Irish
48 Gaelic

Welsh Group
49 Welsh
50 Breton

H ARMENIAN
51 Armenian

I IRANIAN

Northern Group
52 Ossetinian

Persian Group
53 Persian
54 Tatic
55 Talyshic

Kurdic Luric Group
56 Kurdish
57 Lurish
58 Bakhtiar
*59 Mamasenian
*60 Kuhkgeluyan

*Eastern Group
61 Tajik
62 Khazara
63 Afghan
64 Baluchi

II URALIC

K FINNIC

Northwest Group
65 Finnish
66 Karelian
67 Vepsian
68 Izhorian (Ingrian)
69 Vodian
70 Estonian
71 Livian

Northeast Group
72 Komian (Zyrian)
73 Komi-Permian
74 Udmurtian (Votiak)

Southeast or Volga Group
75 Marian (Cheremissian)
76 Mordvinian-Moksha
77 Mordvinian-Erzia

L SAMOYEDIC
78 Nenets-Samoyedic

M LAPP
79 Lapponian

N UGRIAN
80 Hungarian
81 Khanty-Ostiak
82 Mansi-Vogul

III ALTAIC

O TURKIC

Northwest (Kipchak) Group
83 Karachay
84 Balkar
85 Nogay
86 Kumyk
87 Bashkir
88 Kazakh
*89 Kara-Kalpak
*90 Kirghiz
*91 Altayan
92 Tatar or Tartar

Southwest (Oguz) Group
93 Osman Turks
94 Gagauz
95 Azerbayjanian
96 Turkmenian

*Southeast (Kashgar) Group
97 Uzbek

Turks of S.W. Asia
98 Afshar, Ajar
*99 Kashkay
100 Karapapakh

Chuvash Group
101 Chuvashian

P MONGOLIC
102 Kalmuckian

IV SEMITIC
103 Arabic
104 Assyrian
105 Maltese

V HAMITIC
106 Berberian

VI CAUCASIC

S NORTHWEST GROUP
Circassian
Kabardinian
Abkhasian

T NORTH CENTRAL (VEYNAKH) GROUP
Ingushian
Chechenian

V NORTHEAST (DAGHESTAN) Group
Avarian
Darginian
Lakian
Tabassaranian
Lesginian (Kurinian)

W SOUTHERN (GEORGIAN) GROUP
Swanian or Swanetian
Mingrelian
Lazian
Georgian (Kartwel)

VII BASQUE
107 Basque

*Not shown on map

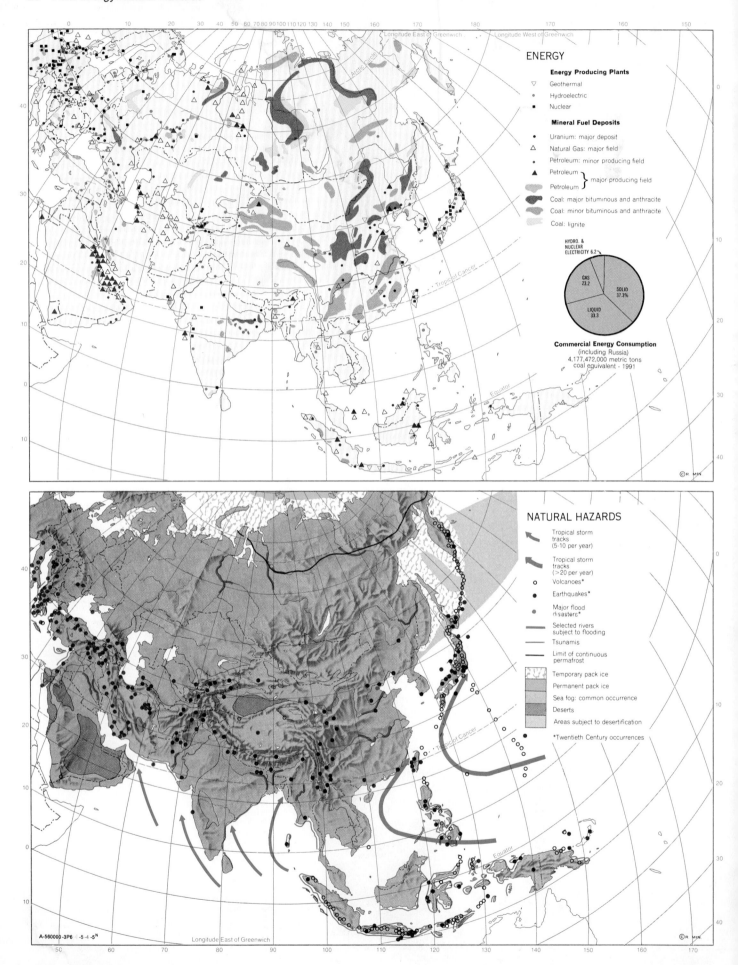

ENERGY

Energy Producing Plants

▽ Geothermal
● Hydroelectric
■ Nuclear

Mineral Fuel Deposits

• Uranium: major deposit
△ Natural Gas: major field
• Petroleum: minor producing field
▲ Petroleum ⎫
⎬ major producing field
▓ Petroleum ⎭
▒ Coal: major bituminous and anthracite
▒ Coal: minor bituminous and anthracite
░ Coal: lignite

HYDRO. & NUCLEAR ELECTRICITY 6.2

GAS 23.2

SOLID 37.3%

LIQUID 33.3

Commercial Energy Consumption
(including Russia)
4,177,472,000 metric tons
coal equivalent · 1991

© R MN

NATURAL HAZARDS

➤ Tropical storm tracks (5-10 per year)
➤ Tropical storm tracks (>20 per year)
○ Volcanoes*
● Earthquakes*
● Major flood disasters*
━ Selected rivers subject to flooding
━ Tsunamis
━ Limit of continuous permafrost
▒ Temporary pack ice
▒ Permanent pack ice
▒ Sea fog: common occurrence
▒ Deserts
░ Areas subject to desertification

● *Twentieth Century occurrences

Longitude East of Greenwich

© R MN

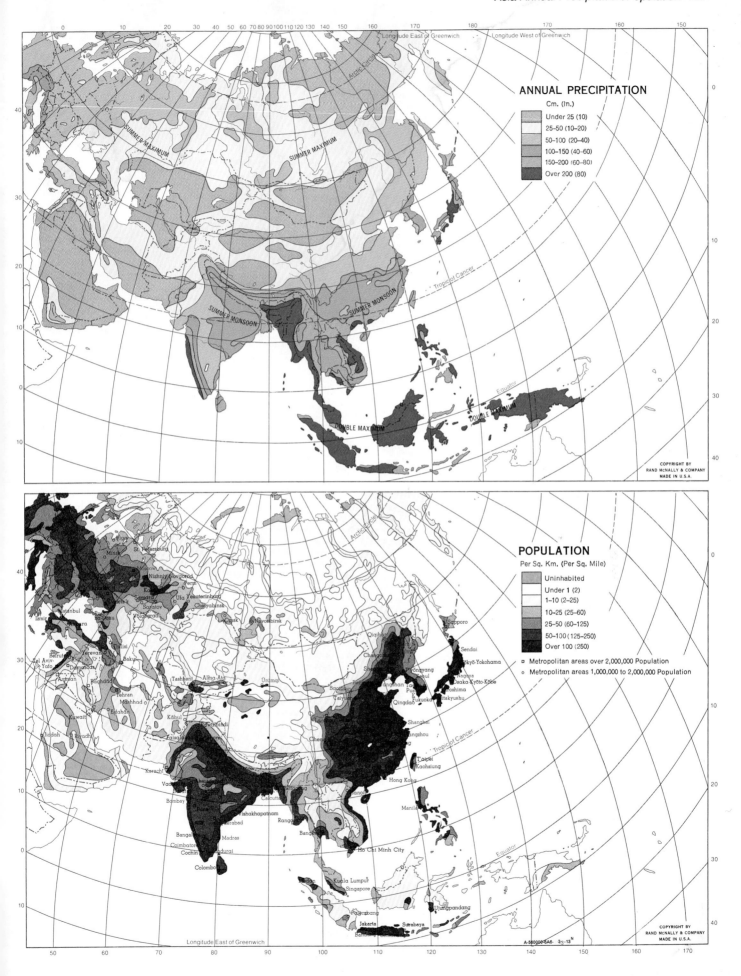

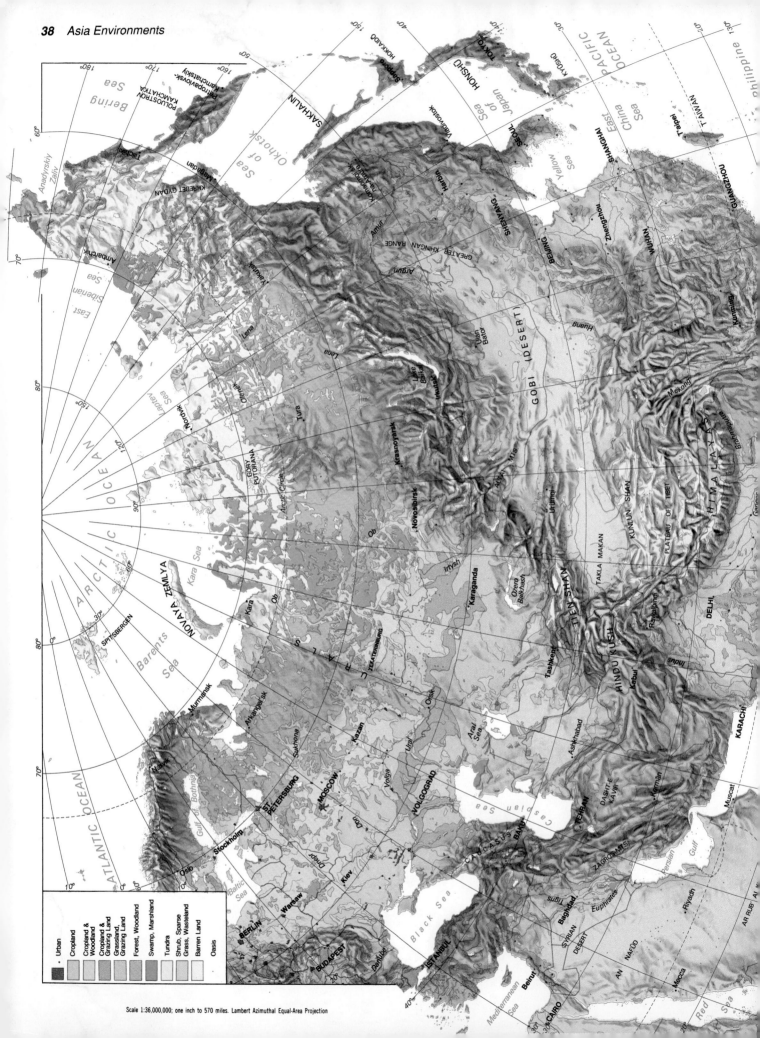

38 Asia Environments

Scale 1:36,000,000; one inch to 570 miles. Lambert Azimuthal Equal-Area Projection

Urban
Cropland
Cropland & Woodland
Cropland & Grazing Land
Grassland, Grazing Land
Forest, Woodland
Swamp, Marshland
Tundra
Shrub, Sparse Grass, Wasteland
Barren Land
Oasis

South China Sea

MINDANAO
Cebu
Celebes Sea
Manado
CELEBES
Kota Kinabalu
BORNEO
Kuching
Ujung Pandang
Java Sea
JAKARTA
JAVA
SINGAPORE
SUMATRA
Medan
HO CHI MINH CITY
BANGKOK
Rangoon
Andaman Sea
Equator
Bay of Bengal
SRI LANKA
MADRAS
Colombo
WESTERN GHATS
EASTERN GHATS
Calicut
BOMBAY
INDIAN OCEAN
Arabian Sea
Gulf of Aden
Berbera

| 0 | 100 | 200 | 400 | 600 | 800 Miles |
| 0 | 150 | 300 | 600 | 900 | 1200 Kilometers |

JAPAN
Tokyo
Osaka
NORTH KOREA
Pyongyang
SOUTH KOREA
Seoul
Harbin
RUSSIA
Moscow
Novosibirsk
Ulan Bator
MONGOLIA
Beijing
Shanghai
CHINA
Wuhan
Chongqing
Guangzhou
HONG KONG
MACAO
TAIWAN
Taipei
PHILIPPINES
Manila
INDONESIA
Jakarta
Equator
VIETNAM
LAOS
Hanoi
Ho Chi Minh City
THAILAND
Bangkok
CAMBODIA
Phnom Penh
MALAYSIA
Kuala Lumpur
SINGAPORE
BRUNEI
BURMA
Rangoon
Kathmandu
NEPAL
BHUTAN
BANGLADESH
Dhaka
INDIA
New Delhi
Calcutta
Bombay
Madras
Lhasa
Ürümqi
KAZAKHSTAN
Almaty
UZBEKISTAN
Tashkent
KYRGYZSTAN
Bishkek
TAJIKISTAN
Dushanbe
TURKMENISTAN
Ashkhabad
AFGHANISTAN
Kabul
PAKISTAN
Islamabad
Karachi
IRAN
Tehran
SRI LANKA
Colombo
OMAN
Muscat
UNITED ARAB EMIRATES
QATAR
Riyadh
SAUDI ARABIA
YEMEN
San'a'
Aden
IRAQ
Baghdad
KUWAIT
Kuwait
SYRIA
TURKEY
Ankara
Istanbul
AZERBAIJAN
Baku
ARMENIA
GEORGIA
Tbilisi
CYPRUS
LEBANON
ISRAEL
JORDAN
POLITICAL
Tropic of Cancer
Longitude East of Greenwich

TURKMENISTAN
Ashkhabad
Meshhed
Kerman
IRAN
Tehran
Shiraz
Abadan
OMAN
Muscat
Dubayy
Abu Dhabi
UNITED ARAB EMIRATES
Ad Dawhah
QATAR
BAHRAIN
Al Manamah
Riyadh
KUWAIT
Kuwait
Al Basrah
IRAQ
Baghdad
SAUDI ARABIA
Mecca
Al Madinah
Tropic of Cancer
YEMEN
San'a'
Aden
SYRIA
TURKEY
Ankara
Adana
Erzurum
ARMENIA
AZERBAIJAN
Baku
Tabriz
Bakhtaran
Damascus
Beirut
LEBANON
CYPRUS
ISRAEL
Jerusalem
Amman
JORDAN
POLITICAL

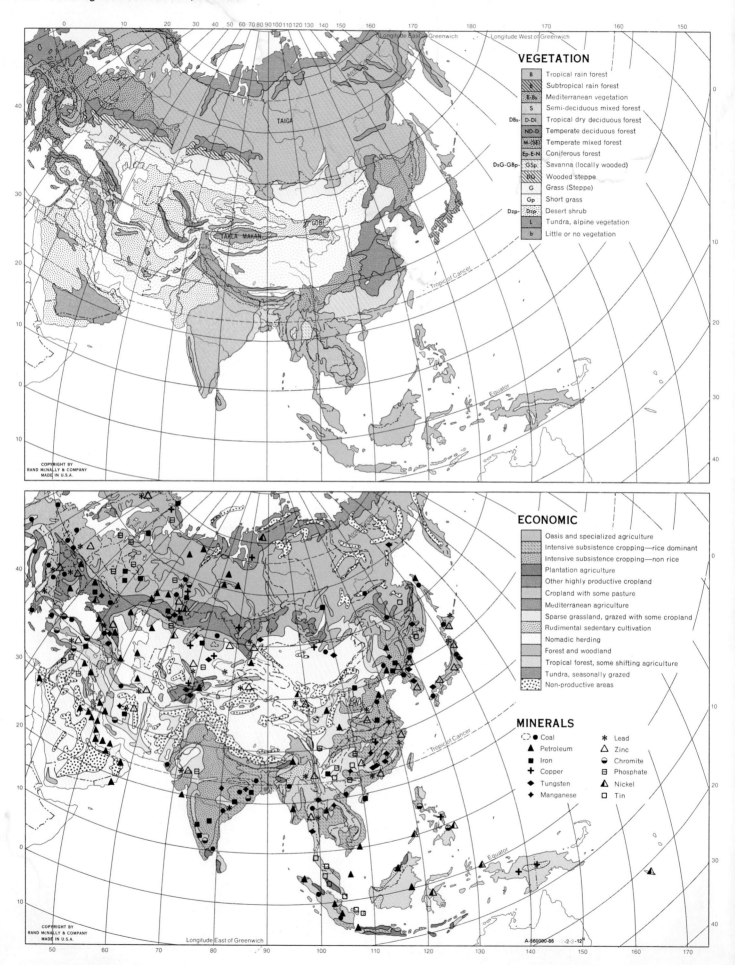

VEGETATION

B	Tropical rain forest
B	Subtropical rain forest
B-Bs	Mediterranean vegetation
S	Semi-deciduous mixed forest
DBs- D-Di	Tropical dry deciduous forest
ND-D	Temperate deciduous forest
M-(SE)	Temperate mixed forest
Ep-E-N	Coniferous forest
DsG-GBp- GSp	Savanna (locally wooded)
DG	Wooded steppe
G	Grass (Steppe)
Gp	Short grass
Dzp- Dzp	Desert shrub
L	Tundra, alpine vegetation
b	Little or no vegetation

ECONOMIC

	Oasis and specialized agriculture
	Intensive subsistence cropping—rice dominant
	Intensive subsistence cropping—non rice
	Plantation agriculture
	Other highly productive cropland
	Cropland with some pasture
	Mediterranean agriculture
	Sparse grassland, grazed with some cropland
	Rudimental sedentary cultivation
	Nomadic herding
	Forest and woodland
	Tropical forest, some shifting agriculture
	Tundra, seasonally grazed
	Non-productive areas

MINERALS

●	Coal	✳	Lead
▲	Petroleum	△	Zinc
■	Iron	◖	Chromite
✛	Copper	⊟	Phosphate
◆	Tungsten	◭	Nickel
◆	Manganese	◻	Tin

Longitude East of Greenwich

A-560000-86 -2-3-12

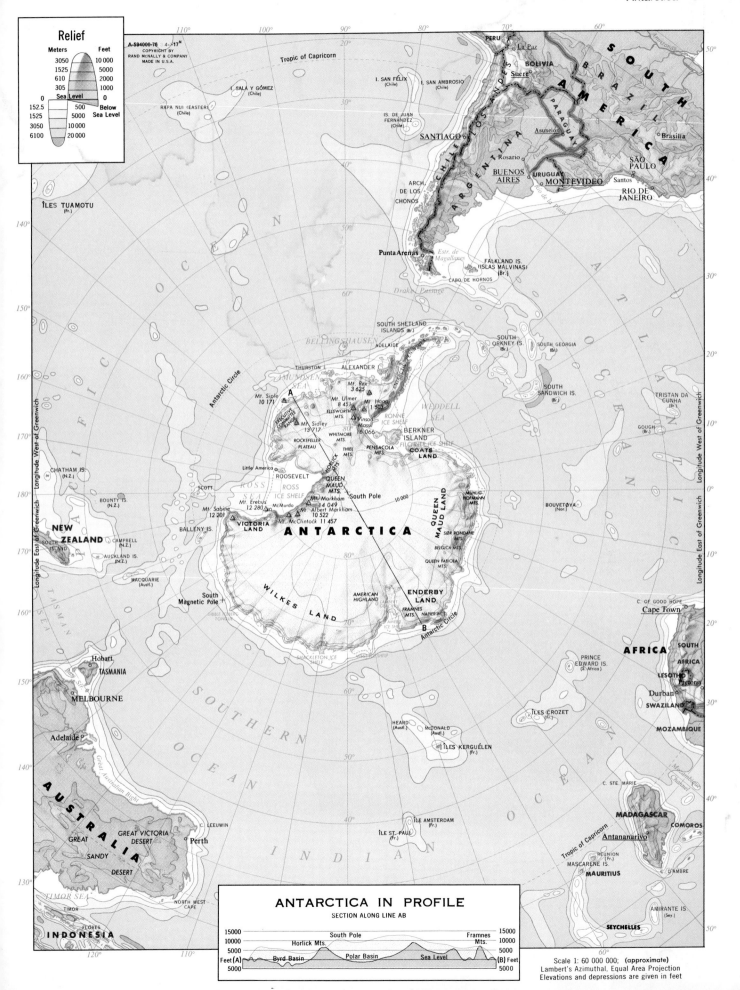

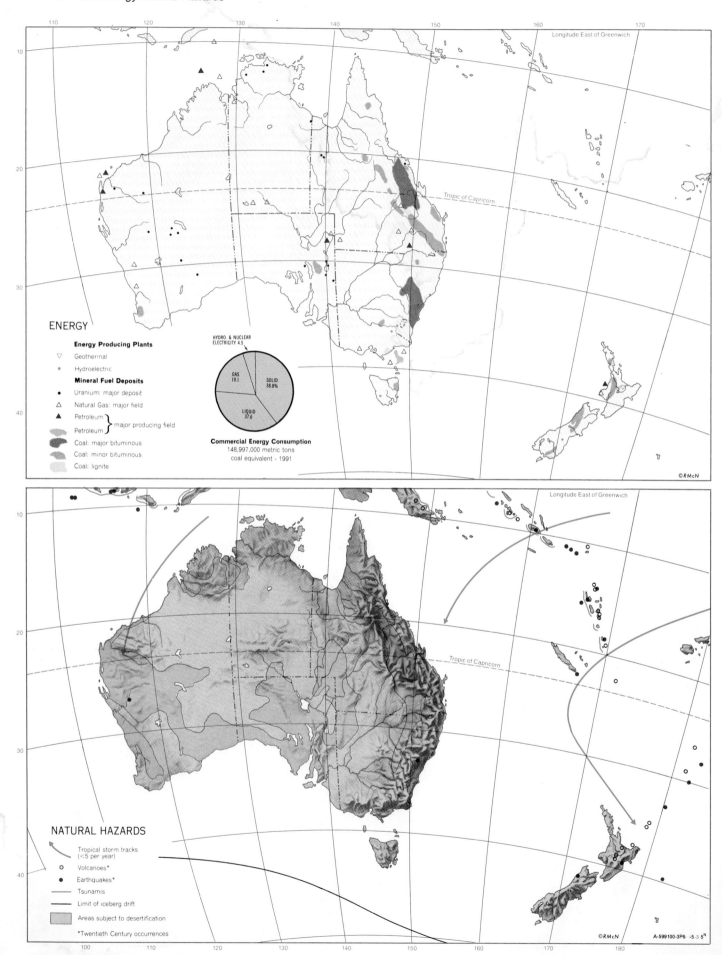

ENERGY

Energy Producing Plants

▽ Geothermal

● Hydroelectric

Mineral Fuel Deposits

● Uranium: major deposit

△ Natural Gas: major field

▲ Petroleum

Petroleum ⎬ major producing field

Coal: major bituminous

Coal: minor bituminous

Coal: lignite

HYDRO. & NUCLEAR
ELECTRICITY 4.5

GAS
19.1

SOLID
38.8%

LIQUID
37.6

Commercial Energy Consumption
148,997,000 metric tons
coal equivalent - 1991

Longitude East of Greenwich

Tropic of Capricorn

©RMcN

NATURAL HAZARDS

⤴ Tropical storm tracks
(<5 per year)

○ Volcanoes*

● Earthquakes*

⎯ Tsunamis

⎯ Limit of iceberg drift

Areas subject to desertification

*Twentieth Century occurrences

Longitude East of Greenwich

Tropic of Capricorn

©RMcN   A-599100-3P6 --5-3 5ᴺ

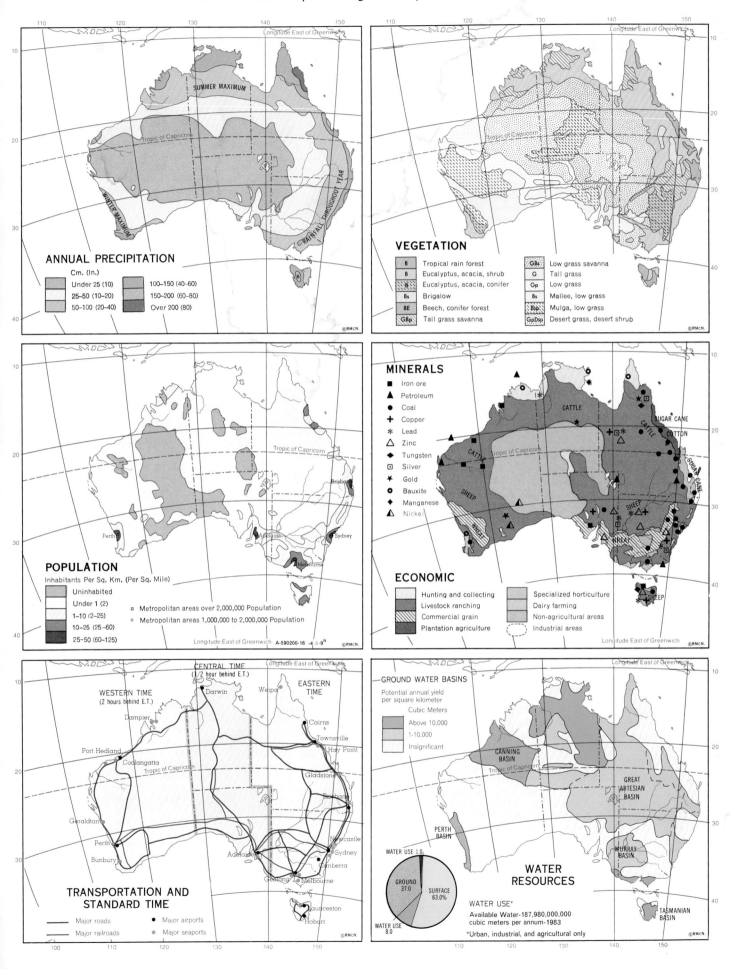

ANNUAL PRECIPITATION

Cm. (In.)

- Under 25 (10)
- 25–50 (10–20)
- 50–100 (20–40)
- 100–150 (40–60)
- 150–200 (60–80)
- Over 200 (80)

SUMMER MAXIMUM
WINTER MAXIMUM
RAINFALL THROUGHOUT YEAR
Tropic of Capricorn

VEGETATION

B	Tropical rain forest	GBs	Low grass savanna
B	Eucalyptus, acacia, shrub	G	Tall grass
B	Eucalyptus, acacia, conifer	Gp	Low grass
Bs	Brigalow	Bs	Mallee, low grass
BE	Beech, conifer forest	Bsp	Mulga, low grass
GBp	Tall grass savanna	GpDsp	Desert grass, desert shrub

POPULATION

Inhabitants Per Sq. Km. (Per Sq. Mile)

- Uninhabited
- Under 1 (2)
- 1–10 (2–25)
- 10–25 (25–60)
- 25–50 (60–125)

▫ Metropolitan areas over 2,000,000 Population
◦ Metropolitan areas 1,000,000 to 2,000,000 Population

Perth   Adelaide   Sydney   Brisbane   Melbourne

Longitude East of Greenwich   A-590200-16 -4-5-9ᴺ

MINERALS

- ■ Iron ore
- ▲ Petroleum
- ● Coal
- + Copper
- ✳ Lead
- △ Zinc
- ◆ Tungsten
- ▫ Silver
- ✶ Gold
- ○ Bauxite
- ◆ Manganese
- ▲ Nickel

CATTLE   SUGAR CANE   COTTON   SHEEP   WHEAT

ECONOMIC

- Hunting and collecting
- Livestock ranching
- Commercial grain
- Plantation agriculture
- Specialized horticulture
- Dairy farming
- Non-agricultural areas
- Industrial areas

Longitude East of Greenwich

TRANSPORTATION AND STANDARD TIME

WESTERN TIME (2 hours behind E.T.)
CENTRAL TIME (1/2 hour behind E.T.)
EASTERN TIME

Darwin   Weipa   Cairns   Townsville   Hay Point   Gladstone   Brisbane   Newcastle   Sydney   Canberra   Geelong   Melbourne   Adelaide   Bunbury   Perth   Geraldton   Coolangatta   Port Hedland   Dampier   Launceston   Hobart

Tropic of Capricorn

- —— Major roads
- —— Major railroads
- ● Major airports
- ● Major seaports

WATER RESOURCES

GROUND WATER BASINS

Potential annual yield per square kilometer
Cubic Meters

- Above 10,000
- 1–10,000
- Insignificant

CANNING BASIN   GREAT ARTESIAN BASIN   PERTH BASIN   MURRAY BASIN   TASMANIAN BASIN

WATER USE 1.0
GROUND 37.0   SURFACE 63.0%
WATER USE 8.0

WATER USE*
Available Water-187,980,000,000 cubic meters per annum-1983

*Urban, industrial, and agricultural only

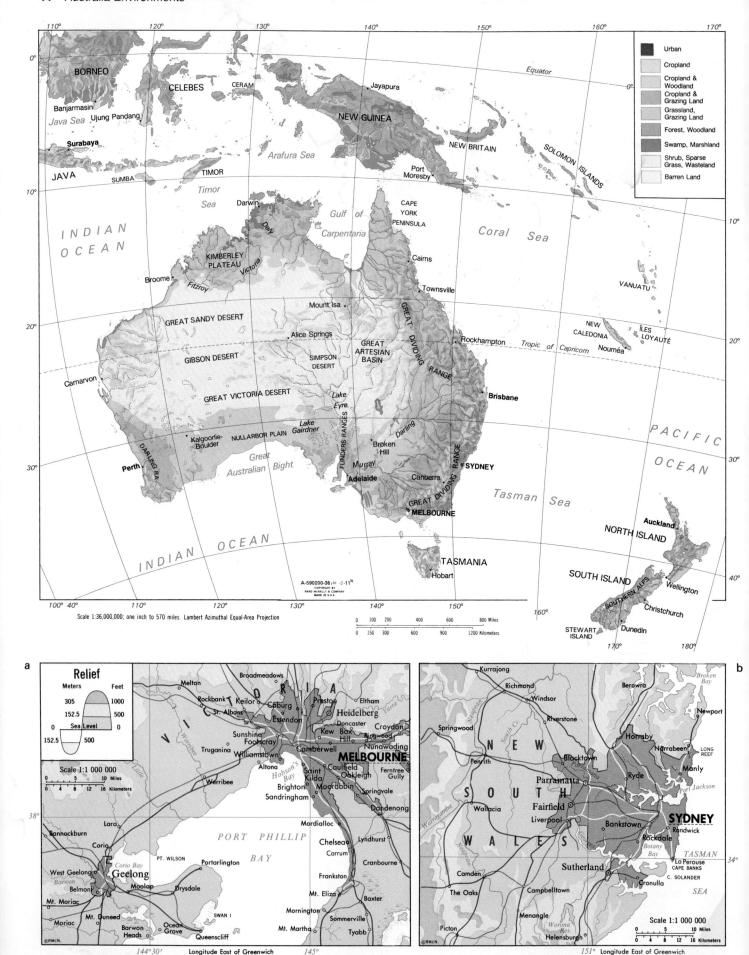

Scale 1:36,000,000; one inch to 570 miles. Lambert Azimuthal Equal-Area Projection

Urban
Cropland
Cropland & Woodland
Cropland & Grazing Land
Grassland, Grazing Land
Forest, Woodland
Swamp, Marshland
Shrub, Sparse Grass, Wasteland
Barren Land

a

Relief

Meters	Feet
305	1000
152.5	500
0 Sea Level	0
152.5	500

Scale 1:1 000 000

b

Longitude East of Greenwich

Longitude East of Greenwich

Scale 1:1 000 000

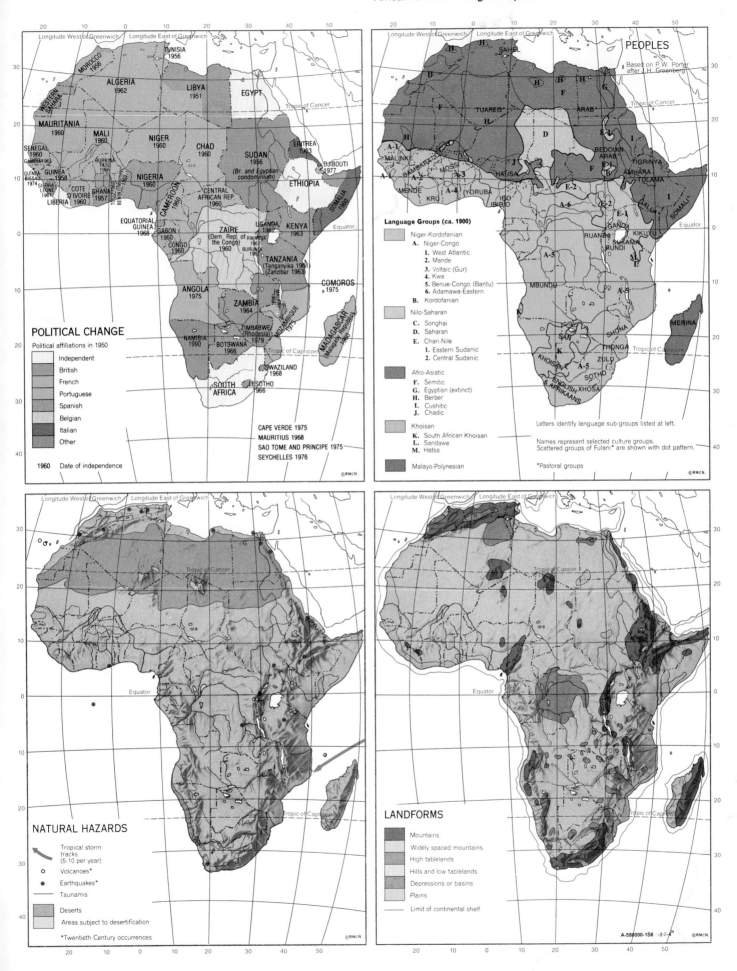

POLITICAL CHANGE

Political affiliations in 1950

- Independent
- British
- French
- Portuguese
- Spanish
- Belgian
- Italian
- Other

1960 Date of independence

CAPE VERDE 1975
MAURITIUS 1968
SAO TOME AND PRINCIPE 1975
SEYCHELLES 1976

©RMCN.

PEOPLES

Based on P.W. Porter
after J.H. Greenberg

Language Groups (ca. 1900)

- Niger-Kordofanian
  - A. Niger-Congo
    1. West Atlantic
    2. Mande
    3. Voltaic (Gur)
    4. Kwa
    5. Benue-Congo (Bantu)
    6. Adamawa-Eastern
  - B. Kordofanian
- Nilo-Saharan
  - C. Songhai
  - D. Saharan
  - E. Chari-Nile
    1. Eastern Sudanic
    2. Central Sudanic
- Afro-Asiatic
  - F. Semitic
  - G. Egyptian (extinct)
  - H. Berber
  - I. Cushitic
  - J. Chadic
- Khoisan
  - K. South African Khoisan
  - L. Sandawe
  - M. Hatsa
- Malayo-Polynesian

Letters identify language sub-groups listed at left.

Names represent selected culture groups.
Scattered groups of Fulani* are shown with dot pattern.

*Pastoral groups

©RMCN.

NATURAL HAZARDS

- Tropical storm tracks (5-10 per year)
- ○ Volcanoes*
- ● Earthquakes*
- Tsunamis
- Deserts
- Areas subject to desertification

*Twentieth Century occurrences

©RMCN.

LANDFORMS

- Mountains
- Widely spaced mountains
- High tablelands
- Hills and low tablelands
- Depressions or basins
- Plains
- Limit of continental shelf

A-589000-1S6 -3-2-A

©RMCN.

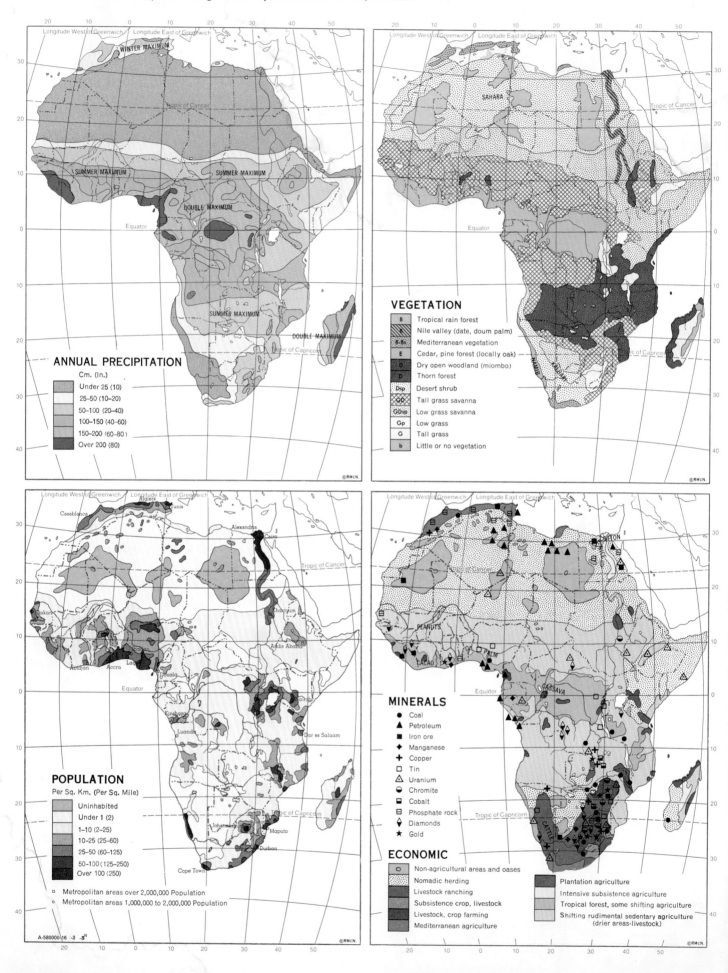

ANNUAL PRECIPITATION
Cm. (In.)
- Under 25 (10)
- 25–50 (10–20)
- 50–100 (20–40)
- 100–150 (40–60)
- 150–200 (60–80)
- Over 200 (80)

VEGETATION
B	Tropical rain forest
R	Nile valley (date, doum palm)
B-Bs	Mediterranean vegetation
E	Cedar, pine forest (locally oak)
D	Dry open woodland (miombo)
D	Thorn forest
Dsp	Desert shrub
GD	Tall grass savanna
GDsp	Low grass savanna
Gp	Low grass
G	Tall grass
b	Little or no vegetation

POPULATION
Per Sq. Km. (Per Sq. Mile)
- Uninhabited
- Under 1 (2)
- 1–10 (2–25)
- 10–25 (25–60)
- 25–50 (60–125)
- 50–100 (125–250)
- Over 100 (250)

▫ Metropolitan areas over 2,000,000 Population
○ Metropolitan areas 1,000,000 to 2,000,000 Population

A-580000-16 -3 -9ᴺ

MINERALS
- ● Coal
- ▲ Petroleum
- ■ Iron ore
- ◆ Manganese
- ✚ Copper
- ◻ Tin
- △ Uranium
- ◌ Chromite
- ⊟ Cobalt
- ⊞ Phosphate rock
- ◊ Diamonds
- ★ Gold

ECONOMIC
⊙	Non-agricultural areas and oases
	Nomadic herding
	Livestock ranching
	Subsistence crop, livestock
	Livestock, crop farming
	Mediterranean agriculture
	Plantation agriculture
	Intensive subsistence agriculture
	Tropical forest, some shifting agriculture
	Shifting rudimental sedentary agriculture (drier areas-livestock)

Urban
Cropland
Cropland & Woodland
Cropland & Grazing Land
Grassland, Grazing Land
Forest, Woodland
Swamp, Marshland
Shrub, Sparse Grass, Wasteland
Barren Land
Oasis

A-580000-36 -2 3-9ᴺ
COPYRIGHT BY
RAND MCNALLY & COMPANY
MADE IN U.S.A.

Scale 1:36,000,000; one inch to 570 miles. Lambert Azimuthal Equal-Area Projection

0 100 200   400   600   800 Miles
0 150 300   600   900   1200 Kilometers

INDEX